GOOD

GOOD STUFF

DENNIS GUNNING

HUTCHINSON
London Sydney Auckland Johannesburg

First published in 1989 by Hutchinson

Paperback edition published 1990

Century Hutchinson Ltd
20 Vauxhall Bridge Road, London SW1V 2SA

Century Hutchinson Australia (Pty) Ltd
20 Alfred Street, Milsons Point, Sydney NSW 2061

Century Hutchinson New Zealand Limited
PO Box 40–086, Glenfield, Auckland 10, New Zealand

Century Hutchinson South Africa (Pty) Ltd
PO Box 337, Bergvlei, 2012 South Africa

Set in 11/13 Baskerville by 𝐅\ Tek Art Ltd, Croydon
Printed and bound in Great Britain by
The Guernsey Press Co. Ltd., Guernsey, Channel Islands.

A CIP catalogue record for this book is available from the British Library

ISBN 009 174357 5

To S. M. G.

The critical acclaim which greeted Peter Kipling's first novel *Grey Journey* is now a matter of literary history. *Tent Pegs* followed and *Quiet Tiger* completed the trilogy, establishing Kipling's monumental account of a northern working-class childhood and growth to manhood as a landmark of post-war English literature. Yet throughout the uniformly enthusiastic critical reception of the novels runs a thread which, quite unwittingly, does less than justice to Peter Kipling. A distinguished critic writing in the *Observer* provides a good example: 'The whole trilogy, and most majestically of all, arguably, perhaps, *Grey Journey* has a quality of smooth inevitability. It is, in a sense, rather like the Rhône below Avignon – inexorable, calm, utterly self-assured, yet with a feral strength which will not be denied.' Another distinguished critic singled out Kipling's dialogue for particular praise in the following terms: 'There's a lot of it. But then there's a lot of the Pacific Ocean. More to the point, his dialogue has an elegance and conviction that is surpassed in English only by very early Meredith and very late Anthony Powell. Outside English one would have to look to Tchekov or some of Bashevis Singer's Yiddish stories for fair comparison. . . [the dialogue] has the smoothness of a brown snake zooming down a rathole and at the same time a stinging truthfulness, a resonance sharp enough to make your sinus tracts ache.'

These critics are representative, I think, both in their generosity and in their unspoken implication, through their use of terms such as 'smoothness' and 'self-assured' that the act of literary creation came easily to Kipling. Such was most emphatically not the case, and to assume so does this fine writer less than justice, as this book aims to show.

If we take first the matter of dialogue. One of the passages of *Grey Journey* best known and most quoted, precisely for the moving and truthful quality of its dialogue, is that in which the central figure, Paul Kane, goes to tell his old ex-miner grandfather that he has won an Exhibition to 'Cornwall' College, Oxford, and will soon leave the mining community which has nurtured him to enter an alien world. By a fortunate chance, Kipling's very first rough draft of this emotionally charged scene has been preserved, and reads as follows:

> Paul fiddled a little longer than was strictly necessary with the faulty catch on Grandad's door. He had gone through this little pantomime ever since he could remember – partly to make something to talk about to the old man, partly to delay for another second or two having to talk to the old man at all. Grandad's watery blue eyes, his slow speech, his bent body, spoke of decades of unknowable, unimaginable physical toil and hardship which made even the life of Paul's father seem soft by comparison. Paul was never easy in Grandad's company, always eager to be away. Grandad knew it, and Paul knew that he knew.
>
> 'That latch of yours still wants fixing, Grandad,' Paul ventured.
>
> 'Nay, na' then by gum!' replied the old man warmly.
>
> 'I have been awarded an Exhibition to Cornwall College, Oxford,' Paul continued.
>
> 'By 'eck, nay, 'ey up!' rejoined Grandad vigorously.
>
> 'An Exhibition does not have quite the same status as an Open Scholarship but is nevertheless a very satisfactory outcome of my scholastic endeavours,' Paul went on.
>
> 'By 'ell, I'll go to t'foot of our stairs,' Grandad expostulated.
>
> 'I hope to do well at Oxford, though I hope that no one here, or indeed elsewhere, will entertain extravagant hopes on my behalf – I can but do my best,' Paul said firmly.
>
> 'Sithee lad, by gum, by 'eck na'then,' cried Gran-

dad, obviously moved. And on that note the interview was concluded.

When Kipling showed me this draft, I sensed that he was not fully satisfied with it and I tactfully ventured to hint as much.

'No, it won't really do. There's something amiss which I can't quite analyse, but I have thought of a way round the difficulties it presents – it is only a minor episode after all,' he said. His second draft of the actual dialogue read thus:

'That latch of yours still wants fixing, Grandad,' Paul shouted.

'Eh?' replied the old man. His profound deafness and obstinate refusal to acquire a hearing aid had often irritated Paul in the past, but now he was deeply grateful for it.

'I'm going to Oxford, more precisely to Cornwall College, to take up an Exhibition,' mouthed Paul.

'You what?' enquired Grandad.

'Well, wish me luck then!' Paul cried mock-heartily.

'By 'eck yon door catch wants fixing, tha' knows by gum,' Grandad observed. And so they parted, as it transpired, forever.

As those familiar with *Grey Journey* will see, we are still some way away from the almost unbearably moving version of this celebrated scene in the final published version, and at this early stage in his development as a writer it must be said that Peter Kipling was sometimes prone to evade his literary problems rather than properly face and wrestle with them. This applied, unfortunately, to plot as well as dialogue. For example, an early draft of a scene in which Paul was to have confronted his family with the fact of his affair with Rebecca (the wife of his Oxford tutor), and her pregnancy by him, read like this.

Paul was resolute at St Pancras, uneasy at Kettering, nervous by Leicester and as the train hissed into

Sheffield station, he was sick with apprehension. He could imagine telling his father. He could imagine telling Aunt Gracie and imagine her knitting needle glare and flood of self-righteous abuse. But his mother – what would she say? He could not begin to imagine. And Uncle Ted. Paul could see him now, very patiently demonstrating how to weight a fishing-line when Paul was eight years old. Uncle Ted. So quiet, so – just plain good, like a fresh brown egg or a dry-stone wall. There was thirty-five minutes to wait at Sheffield before the Mexthorpe train. Thirty-five minutes to think about the exact phrases Paul was going to use to hurt Uncle Ted, and his father and his mother. And Aunt Gracie come to that, knitting-needle eyes and all – how to hurt them beyond measure, beyond forgiveness.

The announcement over the station tannoy was barely comprehensible, 'Will Mister Aul Ane Peese come to the station's mars office.' Paul listened to it three times before he realized that the tin voice was talking to him. In the station master's office, a young policeman was fiddling uneasily with his helmet-strap. He looked past Paul's right shoulder as he spoke.

'I'm afraid I have bad news, Mr Kane – your father was killed in a roof-fall at the colliery this morning, your mother died of a heart attack upon hearing the bad news. Mr Ted Kane, your uncle and Mrs Grace Kane also died this morning, of cerebral haemorrhages, it is believed. Your grandfather also passed away last night in his sleep. I'm sorry. This must all be a bit of a shock, I suppose.'

Relief, guilt, shock and disbelief struggled in Paul's mind as he leafed through the Yellow Pages looking numbly for 'Funeral Directors' in the station phone box.

A good artistic case could be made for this stark way of dealing with the problem posed by the impending and potentially traumatic family confrontation, but unfortunately this was not the only time that Kipling had used sudden death as a plot device at critical moments in these early drafts of *Grey Journey*. Roof-falls, explosions, floods and other mining accidents, for example, featured in all eighteen times in the first draft of the plot, including four major gas explosions in one week. Similarly during a single fortnight at Oxford two of Paul's close friends and also an English don were drowned in the Thames and two girls with whom he was involved emotionally died, roped together in a doomed midnight attempt to scale Magdalen Tower.

The most unlooked for effect of this method of plot-construction, apart from creating an air of melodrama which was utterly remote from Kipling's artistic intentions, was that the novel was turning out to be very short, in the order of five thousand words in fact, and tending if anything to become shorter with each revision. Kipling, indeed, at one point thought of rendering the whole of *Grey Journey* as a poem, perhaps in sonnet form, and I have sometimes wondered a little whether I should have encouraged him in that direction.

Had I done so, however, the English literary world would have lost the actual novel *Grey Journey* and of course *Tent Pegs* and *Quiet Tiger* as well. My part in the whole venture, though, was tiny and peripheral compared with that of Johnson.

Kipling's much-discussed literary co-operation with his neighbour Johnson began merely because Johnson, like 'Paul Kane' but unlike Kipling, had been an undergraduate at Oxford and so Kipling consulted him from time to time on purely technical geographical matters, such as how long it might take to cycle from Worcester College to Queen's and the like. Johnson had often expressed a wish to see or hear something of the as yet untitled novel and eventually Kipling felt that out of mere politeness he ought to let Johnson have his way.

'Perhaps,' said Kipling tentatively one day, 'you might

like to actually read through this little bit, just to check the distances and times and so on?' Thus casually was born the co-operative effort without which *Grey Journey* might either never have seen publication, or at best would have reached the library shelves as just another 'quite promising first novel'.

The Foundations

The 'little bit' which Kipling showed to Johnson was the passage, finally published in *Tent Pegs*, in which Paul Kane tells Elaine, the love of his first year at Oxford, that despite their strong physical attraction to each other, the social gulf between them is so great that Paul feels they must part. The draft which Johnson saw read as follows:

> Paul and Elaine had somehow never formed the habit of walking hand in hand and now he was deeply glad of it. He was also grateful for the fact that when you walk side by side with someone you can't see their eyes.
>
> They did not slacken stride. She did not speak. From a little distance they must have looked like any undergraduate and his girl out for a stroll, the man bespectacled and a few inches the taller, the man doing all the talking, as usual.
>
> The distance from Christ Church Cathedral to the Tom Tower gate was enough for Paul to re-emphasize that he was attracted to Elaine, physically, as strongly as ever and the distance from Tom Tower to Carfax was adequate for him to explain that the social gulf between himself, a Yorkshire miner's son and Elaine, daughter of a somewhat conservative country landowner in Wiltshire, was so great that they ought to end their relationship before further tension, conflict and unhappiness arose. At Carfax, for Paul had carefully planned it thus, they were able to go their separate ways, Elaine to St Hilda's, Paul to Cornwall College (see sketch-map).

'Well,' said Johnson, 'the times and distances sound OK if memory serves – but – you don't mind me saying this? It's a bit, well, flat, don't you feel?'

'Well,' said Kipling in turn, 'I had first thought that Elaine or Paul himself perhaps might be struck by falling masonry from some part of Christ Church – she fatally, he with the effect of blotting out all his memories of the previous few months . . .'

'That would certainly liven it up – and yet – you don't mind me saying this sort of thing?'

'Not at all, please feel quite free.'

'What if perhaps both of them could be simultaneously struck down? – but in that case it would have to be something like a long pole. Maybe scaffolding? You would hardly get two chunks of masonry dropping off the front of Christ Church at one go. Not too plausible that, really. But a pole would do.'

'Frankly,' said Kipling, 'I don't find the plausible plotting of actual events very easy at all. It all, well, unravels so, if you're not careful. For instance – if I might impose?' Johnson nodded encouragingly. 'Well, I thought it would be rather telling if Paul, that's the hero, was from an early age by a genetic fluke taller and generally sturdier than his elder brother, Richard – Richard goes down the mine at fifteen you see – so Paul's latent guilt at not wanting to go down the mine would be constantly prodded by people passing remarks about what a big chap he is getting to be, bigger than his elder brother, what a grand collier he'll make and so on. Then when I looked back through the story I saw there were several references to Richard's handing down clothes to Paul. Poverty you see. Now, having Paul hand clothing up as it were, to Richard seemed rather odd – so I decided to have clothes handed down from Richard to Paul and then lengthened. It served the turn and solved the immediate problem but, as you can imagine, got me into much unnecessary writing over what seemed at first a very simple point.'

'Also,' said Johnson, 'you can't really lengthen socks.

Or vests. I suppose you could lengthen vests but they still wouldn't fit round the arms. If I could suggest? Perhaps he, i.e. Paul, could be constantly socially embarrassed by busting out of his clothes, i.e. Richard's too small cast-offs. Or, better, what if he retains the habit of wearing his clothes too small when he's fairly grown up – because he doesn't know any different? Then there could be this great symbolic moment when he finds out first day at Oxford that nobody else wears their pants mid-calf and he's really pissed off and alienated and everything?'

'Thank you for the suggestion. Even I had not realized that the consequences of making Paul taller than his older brother could be so potentially complex,' said Kipling, a shade coolly.

'Still, leave that, it's a minor point,' said Johnson. 'On plotting problems generally, what about a card index? Seriously. Think about it. If somebody say, climbs a flight of stairs in a story, what can they do? They can get to the top, get to the top and come down again, get half-way up and change their minds and come down, get half-way up and fall down the stairs and so on. Large number of possibilities, but finite, not more than thirty at a guess. So, why not try this? Read novels, note all references in novels to climbing of stairs, make card index of same, select wisely and there you are.'

Kipling smiled. 'I do have rather more complex transactions to deal with than people going up and down stairs.'

'Right OK, take people, types of people in books. Take, say, railway porters in books. What do they do? They carry bags, whistle, behave in a surly fashion, get tips, tell you the way to places with a cheery grin, look strangely at you. That's about it, really, for porters. So here's your bit of plot with a porter, I get off the train, blah, blah, the cheery porter whistled as he carried my bags. "Thank 'ee sir," he cried with a cheery grin as I tipped him a sovereign. But when I asked the way to Castle Rackrent, he looked strangely surly, blah, blah, sort of thing.'

'You don't surely mean I should make a mere pastiche of literary clichés and plot fragments?' Kipling was clearly shocked.

'Well, this way, at least I've got my hero off the train, complete with his luggage,' retorted Johnson, 'and when he asked the porter the way to the castle a gargoyle didn't fall on anybody's head.'

'Yes, yes, I've taken your point, believe me. Your episode, brief and extempore as it was, has some plausibility and that is precisely what my work tends to lack. But surely just, well, cribbing and scissors and paste isn't the way?'

'Look. Try it. Take the parting from Elaine scene, make a serious study in literature and make a proper list of the kind of things birds do or say when the hero tells them goodbye. Then write your own stuff. Make it your very own, but with a bit of helpful guidance, that's all. See how it comes out. Then show it to me if you like. Where's the harm?'

Kipling undertook with considerable reluctance to try this approach to composition and a few weeks later showed Johnson the following version of the Elaine episode, together with the notes of guidance he had collected from his study of appropriate literature (notes which I reproduce here for interest).

Notes on behaviour of girls (rejected) 1. Die mysteriously (only one instance – *End of the Affair* – idiosyncratic?) 2. Weep. 3. Slap face (of man). 4. Kill themselves. 5. Turn on heel. 6. Slam door. 7. Try but fail to kill themselves. 8. Marry someone else. 9. Walk away. 10. Hit man with heavy object (various). 11. Sometimes hit man with object fatally. 12. Shoot man. 13. Fight back tears. 14. Shake hands (very rare).

Paul chose to tell Elaine out of doors. He reasoned (weasel-cowardly as ever, he told himself) that out of doors she would not have any heavy object to hand with which to strike him, and he was certain she did not carry a gun. It was a heady, scented North Oxford evening. They stood beneath a street lamp, May bugs heavily lurching and clicking around the bowl of light. Paul remembered thinking, 'I'll always remember this.' Cars went by.

'My physical attraction towards you, Elaine, is as powerful as ever,' he began, 'But I fear the social gulf between us is so profound and wide that only friction, unhappiness and ultimately disaster can lie ahead. Therefore, I think it best,' he choked, 'if our relationship ceases.' She fought back her tears for a second, then wept, slapped his face, looked about her for a heavy object to hit him with, failed to find one, turned on her heel and walked away. They did not shake hands.

Paul never knew for sure what became of her. He heard that she had later married Sebastian and attempted suicide but with what success or indeed in which order he did not know.

As Paul walked back to Cornwall College, the May bugs were lurching and clicking round every lamp. Cars passed.

'Zillion times better,' said Johnson. 'The dialogue is a bit one-sided but one thing at a time!'

'It certainly feels better,' said Kipling. 'Look, if I write a bit more – perhaps even go right back to the beginning and restart, could you, I mean, be bothered? I'd be very grateful.'

'Certainly. You zap it out, I'll put it with pleasure through the critical mangle. No punches pulled, mind.'

'No punches pulled,' said Peter Kipling, and immediately with greatly revived zest prepared to adapt the new method to the actual opening of the novel, which at that time amounted to little more than the heading 'Chapter One'.

A Start

After one or two false starts which nevertheless gave rise

10

to much very productive research on working class childhood in the 1940s, Kipling decided to begin the novel at the end, as it were, with the final interview between the adult Paul, now a successful author and lecturer, and his father. This required in the first instance much research into literary fathers, especially mining fathers, the results of which Kipling briefly summarized as follows:

Fathers in literature (special ref. coal miners) 1. Die. 2. Fail to understand feelings and/or aspirations of hero. 3. Thrash hero. 4. Cough (miners especially). 5. Cause social and general embarrassment (to hero). 6. Curse hero. 7. Bless hero. 8. Stick thumbs in braces (very common).

Kipling then clothed this spare skeleton in literary flesh, and read it out to Johnson for comment.

Chapter One

Paul felt the usual prickle of generalized social embarrassment that Sunday afternoon as his father faced him, his back to the fireplace, his thumbs as ever, tucked firmly into his braces. 'Bless thee, lad,' he coughed, 'Bless thee and curse thee too, I've never properly understood thee, God knows, especially since tha' went to yon college and developed them aspirations o' thine. As for fathoming thee from t'emotional point o' view . . .' his voice tailed off. As usual Paul just sat there, feeling he ought to say something – must say something – but knowing that anything he said would sound affected, insincere, meaningless even, to this man who had given him life. And who now embarrassed him. As usual.

'Mind you, I've never thrashed thee when tha' were little, never. Tha' mun say that for me,' Paul's father asserted truthfully. Then with a low moan, he fell forward and died.

Kipling paused at this point, looked up. Johnson said: 'Nice so far. I like the general idea. Straight in, action, a death on page one. Startling but plausible. Great. Just one or two tiny things – this "low moan" bit? It's a bit, well, wimpish, isn't it? Would a bloke who's spent his life down a pit go out on a low moan? What about a snarl?' Kipling tentatively pencilled in ' . . . with a low snarl he fell forward and died', and then read the new version through.

'It doesn't sound quite right,' he said, firmly but uncombatively. 'OK, leave it for now – it's a detail, there's plenty of possible other moan-type words. He could even say something as he falls, just fall forward and say something fairly short and then die. Like "Goodbye". Or something symbolic.'

'Thank you. Very helpful. I'll just leave it blank for now I think. I don't want the death to be a big thing you see, just an arresting opening.'

Johnson let the matter of the death rest as he wished to move on to another, more technical matter.

'Right. Point two. He can't really tuck his thumbs in his braces, you know. If he did they would sort of stretch forward and ping to and fro. The literal-minded sort of reader could get a ridiculous mental picture.' Johnson amplified his objection with a vivid mime of his thumbs hooked into imaginary braces, causing them to stretch forward and ping to and fro.

'Could he not,' asked Kipling, 'grasp the braces with more of a downward motion using the whole hand not just the thumb?'

'Then his trousers would sag,' said Johnson, with an air of someone imparting expertise rather than merely contributing to discussion.

'His trousers would sag and the reader's mind's-eye picture would be even more absurd.'

'I'm sure I have references to the grasping of braces,' said Kipling, glancing towards his card index, 'not necessarily by fathers, as such, but certainly by working-class men.'

'Ah, probably nineteenth-century or Edwardian references. Lawrence? Tressell? They'd have bloody great thick leather braces then, not much give, OK for hooking thumbs in, but Paul's dad croaks in ninety seventy-some so he'd have quite narrow elastic braces. Definitely. Take a tip – make it a belt, or possibly the waistband of self-supporting trousers.'

'Thank you, that's very helpful. Further points?'

'Well point three is very tiny, really – but exactly how do you plan to go on from, er, where you've got to?'

Kipling diffidently produced a further sheet of paper, covered in handwriting. 'Perhaps it would be simplest if I read it out; it's not very legible.'

Paul's father lay there. Paul's mind drifted back. Nostalgia for a working-class childhood is a tired and sentimental cliché of our time, but Paul's memories had an acid sharpness, a separateness that had nothing to do with sentimentality. Not even much to do with the present day Paul, in a way, not the Paul who existed now . . .

Reading torn-up bits of the *Yorkshire Post* by the light of a torch in the outside lavatory. . . That junior school smell of plasticine and cabbage. . . Chapped knees in short grey trousers. And earlier layers of memory – Sitting in a creaking push chair to be taken by his father to see the flags and decorations – VE Day that must have been – and crying because . . . because something immensely trivial, hugely heartbreaking had happened . . . something Paul had completely forgotten, only the tickle of tears, and the stiff little paper Union Jack in his hand stuck in his memory with more power and force than the events of last week . . .'

'I have checked the reference to the *Yorkshire Post* by the way,' said Kipling. 'It had indeed a large working-class readership despite its Conservative sympathies and is actually mentioned by name in *Pit Lad* and *The Silent Tower*. The rough outline of the rest of the chapter goes like this – more on short trousers, balaclavas, leatherette helmets etc., school bully, whippets, sitting on pub doorsteps, little racing carts made from plywood and pram-wheels, discovering *Wind in the Willows* through sympathetic teacher etc., Festival of Britain, train journeys to Filey and so on. Leather straps for opening train windows. Being sick, gas mantles, "Children's Hour". Dried eggs. Tizer.

'My basic problem as you will understand is how to get Paul to grammar school and to Oxford with reasonable speed and yet make full use of all this early childhood background material – believe it or not, I have over four thousand items (he tapped the card index) under "Working-class childhood (pre-teen)"'.

'You do have another problem,' said Johnson bluntly: 'Paul's father is still lying dead at his feet. Isn't he going to like e.g. call an ambulance or something?'

'I think that's not being very constructive.'

'OK, OK, so its destructive. But you've still got your old man lying on your feet in a dead condition and you go into a long production number about sitting in an outside bog on VE Day. What will Paul tell the cops? –

> "I'm sorry officer, I know I should have reported the death of my father sooner but I was just trying to remember the score in the 1946 Cup Final, also he was lying on my legs so I couldn't move . . ."'

'He was not lying on his legs, nor even his feet,' retorted Kipling, though calmly, because he had now fully seen the justice of Johnson's view. 'But I take your point. It clearly won't do quite as it stands.'

There was a silence as they considered the problem. I made them some tea. Kipling took off his spectacles and sat quite still, eyes closed, frowning. Johnson doodled – usually little pictures of ships – or fiddled with his teaspoon, rather irritatingly to my mind. As was to be the pattern in the months ahead, Johnson, who had the more agile though by far the less profound literary imagination, broke the silence first.

'They could both die! The whole book could happen in Paul's head between when he falls off the chair and when he hits the floor – like *Pincher Martin*.'

'Yes. Thank you. But do you not think that the very ingenuity of the device might deflect attention from my main venture, an attempt to depict character and emotion in a working-class setting? All people would remember is that Paul Kane turned out to be dead all the time as indeed that is perhaps what they remember about *Pincher Martin*?'

'Right. Good thinking. Scrub dead. Or dad could not be dead, just ill, and Paul could do all the remembering in the ambulance. Holding his hand.'

Kipling returned to the draft and pencilled in some amendments to the final sentence:

> Then with a low snarl (?) he fell forward very ill, but not dead, near Paul's feet, though not so near as to impede Paul's lunge towards the 'phone . . .

'It sounds a shade contrived,' said Kipling wearily, 'I think I need a completely fresh start.'

'What did your old man actually do?' asked Johnson.

'He was an insurance broker. He's retired of course.' I made them some more tea.

A fresh start

'Right,' said Johnson. 'Thinks. What are we, i.e. you, doing? Writing the story of a working-class kid who grows up, goes to university, gets to feel alienated from his parents and everything. In other words, a life, a sort of autobiography except it isn't really you. So why not play down this episodic, atmospheric stuff? Don't start at the end. Let's have a sober and chronological approach. Monumental. Marmoreal. Morley's *Life of Gladstone*. Go for an epic effect, stately: Tolstoy, Solzhenitsyn echoes. This bloke Paul's life is important. So make it sound important. Start at the beginning like a proper Life. No frills. Glacial. Powerful . . .'

'You mean start at his birth?' asked Kipling.

'Conception!' said Johnson earnestly. 'Your hero actually came into being in the middle of World War

Two, there's a setting for you, the black-out and everything. Put the little sod in a bit of cosmic historical context. Gas masks. Doom. Hitler. Then let him grow up with the atomic age. Universalize. Then the outside bog and Tizer and things can come up naturally, they will be mere echoes of the greater horrors of a Europe racked by war etc.'

'I will need to do some more research,' said Kipling cautiously and indeed spent the next few months preparing himself to write the fresh start and a further month chiselling and honing it before presenting it to Johnson, this time in properly typewritten form treble-spaced so that Johnson had plenty of room for written comments. I should say here that Peter Kipling was born on 23 January 1942 and attributed the same birth date to his hero Paul Kane as will be clear from the following extract from this second draft of the novel's opening chapter.

Chapter One

At thirty minutes past midnight on 8 April 1941 local time, a slightly built middle-aged man sat in a large high room at the Headquarters of the British Army in Egypt. He signed a slip of paper and handed it to another, much younger, man who took it away. The middle-aged man was General Archibald Wavell. The paper was the executive order for the evacuation of the town of Benghazi in face of the advance of Rommel's Afrika Korps. 'In signing that,' Wavell thought, 'I may have signed away my career, lost the war, lost the Empire, saved the Empire, done nothing of significance. But I will certainly have enraged Winston Churchill, Prime Minister, First Lord of the Treasury, Minister of Defence. Certainly that' – Wavell ran through the phrases that tomorrow's signal from Churchill would surely contain – "grave concern . . . vital importance of Benghazi . . . Empire . . . strain every nerve . . . action this day".

'Action this day. Yes. I have on my desk,' thought Wavell, 'signals telling me that the German army is going to invade Yugoslavia (probably in the next few minutes, I should think) that I am to send sixty thousand men to Greece, meanwhile defeating this man Rommel in the desert with what's left. This is quite possibly one of the critical days in the world's history – Cannae. Waterloo. 7 April 1941 – April 8th actually. And what can I actually do? What can you do, Archie Wavell, pen pusher in chief? What would Allenby have done, I wonder?'

He smiled a little because he knew exactly what General Allenby would have done in a case like this with half a world to win or lose but nothing, actually, for a man to do, and General Wavell started to do what General Allenby would have done. At 12.32 a.m. Cairo time 8 April 1941, General Archibald Wavell began to sharpen pencils.

In Berchtesgaden, Germany, at that moment it was one hour earlier, by the clock, still 7 April 1941. At 11.32 on 7 April 1941 the sky over southern Germany was clear, clear of English bombers, clear of cloud. The stars shone almost feverishly brightly as if the earth were a planet without atmosphere.

General Franz Halder, Chief of the German General Staff, first Bavarian and first Catholic to hold that post, was not aware of the sky. He was listening to his death, and his country's death. . .

More precisely, he was listening to his Führer. His Führer was not shouting, not raving, in fact he was in an affable and expansive mood and he was talking about the Japanese; their history; culture; eating habits; their capture of Tsingtao in 1914; their aircraft industry; their climate (surprisingly cool in the northern areas). He had been talking about the Japanese since 9.25 p.m.

There was little unusual in this scene – Franz Halder, botanist and mathematician as well as soldier, recognized and felt for the teacher manqué in Hitler, the compulsion to talk, to teach, and to evade the business in hand. But that frosty South German night at 11.32 p.m. for no reason he could ever later understand or analyse General Franz Halder knew, suddenly that his Führer was insane; that there was nothing he or anyone else in that room could do about it; and that he was deathly afraid.

In New York, USA, in a world still at peace, at that precise moment it was still only 4.32 on the cool but pleasant afternoon of 7 April 1941, George B. Pegram of Columbia University had put in a hard couple of hours. He had a pain in the small of his back and an aching neck. He was also in a very good mood. He had spent two hours reading a paper by a smart young scientist called Urey. Now he had finished, pencilled a tick at the end of it. George Pegram felt entitled to a cup of coffee and a doughnut; he was, thanks to Urey, a significant couple of yards nearer being able to make an atomic bomb.

At that precise moment over Northern England there was dense cloud and a light drizzle. In England it was 10.32 p.m. on 7 April 1941 and at or about that time, quite unknown of course to Pegram, Halder or Wavell, Paul Kane was conceived at 12 Alma Terrace, Mexthorpe, near Sheffield, Yorkshire.

Johnson's written comments on the revised start, apart from one or two small marginal points on punctuation and the like, were as follows.

'Terrific. I particularly like the bit about the stars in Germany. There is a good bit at the start of the *The Case of Sergeant Grischa* about stars and planets but it's not as good as yours. Just two small points of crit. comment.

'Point A. Don't you think Wavell, Halder and Pegram could do a bit more by way of physical activity? It's all a tiny bit static, I think. Perhaps Wavell could go for a camel ride? I'm not sure of the significance of the pencil sharpening but I defer to your research on that one –

perhaps Wavell could sharpen some pencils then go on a moonlight camel ride? General Halder obviously can't do much dramatic in the physical line without attracting unfavourable attention from Hitler, SS guards and so on, but could he fiddle nervously with his Iron Cross (did he have one? Must have surely?). Or if that's not on, how about having his eyes glaze with terror etc., when he realises A.H. is barmy? I'm sure Pegram (who he, by the way?) being a Yank, would practise golf shots in a moment of euphoria. How about letting him go and get the doughnut and coffee from somewhere and then come back and play golf shots at his waste-paper bin? (Or did he have a secretary? Love interest?).

Point B. The actual conception of P.K. Very dramatic, epic etc. – but surely a bit abrupt? I believe you are unkeen on writing the sexy bits, also you may have a bit of difficulty dialogue-wise. But I really think you ought to grasp both of these bulls by the horns without more ado and write a brief, tender love scene for P.K.'s conception. Perhaps Mum and Dad could refer a bit to the world scene emphasizing the epic setting. After all it was pretty optimistic of them to start a sprog when the US weren't even in the war yet – how about presenting it as a sort of heroic defiance of fate thing, new life affirmed in the snarling teeth of the panzers sort of thing? Basically though, super.'

Kipling deferred his reply until he was able to meet Johnson in person and discuss at length some amended versions of the historical scenes and also an entirely new conception scene.

He demurred at introducing action via a camel into the Wavell episode on the grounds that his sources made no mention of the general riding camels, at least not in the spring of 1941, but after some discussion it was agreed amicably that Kipling should end the Wavell scene thus:

At 12.32 a.m., Cairo time, 8 April 1941, General Archibald Wavell began to pace vigorously to and fro across his office, humming the defiant old Scots air 'Scots wha' hae' and sharpening pencil after pencil with swift merciless strokes of a Highland dagger.

General Halder's case presented more difficulty. Kipling, with his strong historical sense, insisted that in the tense atmosphere of Hitler's HQ Halder would be extremely reluctant to draw the Führer's attention upon himself by any overt action at all and wished to settle for Halder uttering inward groans. Johnson would not agree that an 'inward groan' counted as action in normal usage of the word at all, but the various nose-pickings, eye-glazings, sneezes and so on which he suggested were all rejected by Kipling as being either historically implausible or not suited to the seriousness of the theme. In the end, an ingenious compromise allowed Halder to:

> feel a sudden wild longing to rush from the room, leap into his Mercedes staff car and drive through the crystalline South German night, laughing, singing snatches of old Bavarian student songs, his lips curled back in a wolf-like, fixed grin – an impulse of course instantly suppressed.

The revised conception scene gave Kipling difficulty, and had to be very thoroughly planned. I reproduce his notes of self guidance below to illustrate the lengths to which he would go to secure authenticity and vigour, particularly in his dialogue, as well as the first draft of the text itself.

Notes A. Current affairs (additional to war news) April 7/8 1941
British income tax goes to 10 shillings in the pound. 'Song of Bernadette' written. Terylene (Dacron) invented. *Daily Worker* suppressed. Brains Trust first broadcast. Lord Baden-Powell died. James Joyce, Virginia Woolf ditto. Lend-Lease Bill signed. *Cambridge Economic History of Europe* started.
Notes B. Sex in Literature (married couples) (working-class).

Unsatisfactory – (He impotent, she frigid). Embarrassment. Unwillingness to be seen nude (her). Creaking (i.e. Beds). Pregnancy: fear of (her) doesn't care (he). Berates because of failure to achieve pregnancy (he, sometimes both) shoulder straps (hers). Running of fingers (Hers) over chest (his) (NB pyjamas [his] never seem to give rise to difficulty) breasts, cupping of etc. (he) buttocks, seizing of (both) deep sleep (afterwards). Lusting. Matted hair of chest (his). Broad child-bearing hips (her). Lying awake afterwards (she) faint far-away smile (she). Moans (both) 'Rubbers'.

A light drizzle was falling on the Yorkshire mining village of Mexthorpe on that night of 7 April 1941. Alfred and Elsie Kane, at 12 Alma Terrace, had gone to bed early and lay talking softly so as not to awaken their two year old son, Richard. 'At least we're not impudent nor rigid,' said Elsie with a little giggle.

'Ah dunna take thy meaning lass,' rejoined Alfred.

'I read about it,' she averred, 'it means either tha canna, you know, do it, or I don't want to.'

'There's no danger o' that, tha wanton,' breathed Alfred and slipped the strap of her cotton nightdress over her white shoulder to cup her still firm breast.

'But not toneet lass,' he sighed, 'Ah've no rubbers.' Elsie said nothing but ran her fingers through the matted hair of his chest, causing him to moan a little as if in pain.

''Appen there's no need of rubbers 'appen its time young Richard was no longer an only bairn . . .'

'Nae, lass, how can tha think o' such wi income tax up to ten bob i't pound and Rommel at gates o' Benghazi, Balkans about to go up i' flames? What sort o' world is this in which to bear a new born bairn? Ah'm only glad old Baden-Powell didna' live to see it, nor Virginia Woolf nor yon mick with t'gift o' tongues – James Joyce.'

'Does tha not want me, then?' she breathed.

'Tha' knows right well,' and he roughly pulled

down her other shoulder strap and lustily caressed her breasts. 'But 'tis a world o' darkness, sithee!'

'Tha' means t'blackout, love?' She stroked his stomach.

'Nay. But think on. *Daily Worker* suppressed. Even in England now there's no more freedom to speak or write as tha' will.'

'But we take t'*Yorkshire Post* love,' she murmured with a faint, far away smile, caressing him through the thick fabric of his pyjamas.

'It's principle o' t'thing,' he gritted, 't'worlds on t'edge o' t'abyss o' barbarism, and what does t'intelligentsia come up wi' – "Song of Bloody Bernadette",' he growled bitterly.

'Nay, nay lad dunna tek on so. 'Appen Yanks'll come in, like last time, that'd do for old Hitler!'

'Well lass, Lend-Lease is weel enough but it is na' full belligerency, by a long bloody score,' he muttered, but his resolve was weakening as he slid her other shoulder strap down. ''Appen tha's right, though,' he murmured. 'This 'ere new Wireless Brains Trust – t'*New Cambridge Economic History* started. These be but glims o' light – but glims is better than nowt when tha's lost it in t' dark night o' barbarism . . And t'Soviets are yet to show their 'and . . .'

'Come to me man o'mine,' she cried, tearing off his pyjamas in one swift movement. 'Nay, nay tha' wanton,' he cried but already his hands were grasping her wide child-bearing hips, the bed creaking as they came together, 'but if I have thee I'll have thee stark naked' and he brutally ripped away her nightdress so that she moaned beneath him. 'Nay tha' bad 'un, tha' bad 'un,' she gasped, shy still after all this time to make love naked.

'Pay no heed,' he said gently as he entered her. 'I'll get thee a new nightie made o' this novel fabric, Terylene.'

So at 10.32 on the night of 7 April 1941, Paul Kane,

22

was conceived – a product of the power of love to cast a little pale light even in the darkest hours of mankind. Perhaps General Wavell had he known of it, would have felt momentarily, at the very edge of his consciousness, cheered, as by a distant bird song.

As Elsie lay awake for a little afterwards, she did not think of General Wavell nor of Franz Halder, and least of all, of George Pegram.

Johnson read this passage carefully and more slowly than was his habit.

'She's got three shoulder straps,' he said, 'look' and he pointed to the text, 'he slides one down over her white blah-blah, then the other one, then another one yet. Also actually if you think it through, once he had slid down two she wouldn't be able to move her arms freely so she couldn't stroke his stomach. She might even start to feel claustrophobic, you know, confined or whatever, even hysterical unless they had a bondage thing going? How about a bondage thing?'

'But the slipping down of straps was only intended to show Alf becoming gradually aroused and yet at the same time . . . What about buttons? He could undo the buttons of her nightdress one at a time, as many buttons as might be convenient to the narrative.'

'Good thought!' (one could almost sense the creative sparks fly between Kipling and Johnson at that moment). 'But she'd better have a few open to start with.'

'Why?' asked Kipling, momentarily at a loss.

'If he slips open just the top button of her nightie he can't sort of do much, can he? Except stroke her collar-bone, just. It would take four or five buttons before he could get any steamy type action at all. In fact trying anything much with only one button open he could get cramp in his wrist – how about agonizing cramp in his wrist as a symbol of the impotence of the agonized working class or something?'

'Thank you. I think I will work in the buttons.

Something of the order of three already open, perhaps fallen off because the family could only afford garments of poor quality? Three open, and approximately four, as it were, to go.'

'There is something a bit more basic actually as well.' Johnson said. 'Which is, actually, sorry, but she sounds like a bloody halfwit. It's not a debate they have dammit, it's a WEA lecture. All she really says is "Screw me". No argument, no cut and thrust. Alf doesn't just get all the good lines he gets all the lines, period.'

'She does mention quite appositely the possibility of American intervention in the war,' Kipling observed mildly.

'But she doesn't develop the point, does she? She's just, well, face it, a sex-object.'

'Perhaps,' said Kipling, 'she actually would have been, I mean, somewhat like that. A miner's wife in 1941?'

'Probably was. Probably thick as a boot sole but you can't write her like that, not nowadays. Think of the reviews . . .

"Mr Kipling's otherwise fecund imagination evidently cannot stretch to the idea that a working-class woman could actually be a shade more articulate and intelligent than a pitman's whippet . . . insulting stereotypes . . . chauvinist Klutz, etc."'

'Yes, I do see a possible difficulty from the point of view of the book's critical reception, but surely I should be writing the truth as I see it?'

'Look – suppose you were writing about, say, the Deep South in about 1880 would you have some black man saying

"Us niggers never did like this Yankee freedom stuff. We was happy on de plantation with massa and Miss Maudie and de bloodhounds, de mornin' dew on de magnolia fields an all"?'

'I would certainly have other negro characters who expressed countervailing views, at some point,' said Kipling sharply.

'Right. Double-top. Countervailing views. If you

make Paul's mummy a dumbo you've absolutely got to write in some other woman-type working-class figure who knows what day it is – gets the Nobel prize for chemistry or something. An Auntie, e.g. an auntie who was a suffragette – hey wait a minute, how about that? Or a black auntie?'

'No,' said Kipling, quite firmly, 'sooner than write an entirely new and extraneous character simply to satisfy the prejudices of the day I will write Paul's mother as a reasonably intelligent and articulate woman as she may well have been in fact. Very much the equal of the father. Not superior, you understand, otherwise the parallels with *Sons and Lovers* would be undesirably close. But equal.'

'Great,' said Johnson, 'one more tiny point.'

Johnson's third point concerned the mechanics of Elsie's tearing off of her husband's pyjamas 'in one swift movement'. Well over an hour was spent on this point, and all the solutions suggested by either Kipling or Johnson seemed to have serious flaws. Johnson leaned towards simple, radical answers, such as a night shirt for Alf or initial nudity on his part. Kipling rejected the first on the grounds of incongruity, and the second as being unlikely in that period and social setting. He himself leaned towards pyjamas that had been in some way weakened by frequent washing or, contrariwise, so begrimed by lack of washing as to have become somehow actually greasy and so easily removed. As Johnson doggedly pointed out, though, however slippery and/or flimsy pyjamas might be, they do, in their very nature, have two separate parts and so cannot be removed 'in one swift movement' except perhaps by someone extremely skilled and practised. The possibility of Mrs Kane having such a special skill and whether or not to explain to the reader where she came by it was then discussed, inconclusively.

It was Peter Kipling's sense of history which showed the way out of this minor impasse, and incidentally gave rise to one of the book's most touching little passages, such is the flukish way of creativity.

A few days before the conception scene, it was decided, Elsie Kane would be looking for her husband's pyjamas to wash, and fail to find them. When he returns from the pit, she berates him for having sold or pawned his pyjamas to buy drink or place bets on greyhounds. At first he is evasive, surly even – it is only later that it emerges how, in a wholly characteristic act of rough generosity, he has sent his pyjamas (his only pair) to the Greek Army (at that time fighting the Italians in the freezing and pitiless terrain of Albania) via Lady Astor's Greek Army Relief and Comforts Fund.

Thus as another tiny, infinitesimal consequence of the unfolding world tragedy, Alfred Kane was unwillingly, unusually and for a short period only, until Elsie could knit or otherwise provide him with some form of nightwear, sleeping nude in the early part of April 1941.

The re-written passage, however, was changed in much more radical ways than a mere adjustment of Alfred and Elsie Kane's clothing. The relevant section now read as follows.

'I'm glad tha's not impotent our Alf,' murmured Elsie, 'nor thee frigid,' rejoined her husband, slipping open the fourth button of her nightdress to fondle a still firm breast (the first three buttons being for a variety of reasons either undone or missing) – 'But I've no rubbers lass, so we mun bide tonight.'

'Ah think such a decision should not go just on t' nod,' retorted Elsie stroking the muscles of his chest 'without some preliminary discussion, if tha teks my drift.'

'Nay nay lass, 'ow can we tek t'risk o' a bairn wi' Benghazi ready and ripe to fall and t'Balkans about to go down afore Hitler's Panzers,' moaned Alfred, stirred in spite of himself by the pressure of one of Elsie's broad child-bearing hips against him.

'How does tha' know,' breathed Elsie 'that t'Soviet Union will not tek advantage of 'Itler's embroilment i' t'Balkans to strike across the Vistula?' As she slipped her hand beneath his buttocks, causing the bed to creak, he muttered thickly.

'Yon's nobbut speculation – income tax at ten bob in t'pound, that's present reality. Cultural decay – ' but he slipped open another button, his hands acting almost in spite of themselves.

'Cultural decay,' she challenged, 'what about t' Brains Trust?'

'"Song o' Bloody Bernadette"!' he countered, roughly tearing open another button, 'Suppression o' *Daily Worker* i't very midst o' t'democracy we toil to defend.'

'T'*Cambridge Economic History*,' she breathed huskily, 'nobbut a bit of a reckling thing now, but t'will grow – like our bairn and . .' triumphantly now as she aroused him and could feel his arousal.

'What about Lend-lease, Alf lad?'

''Tisna full American Belligerency and yet – Nay!' – he tore open two more buttons, his lust irresistible – 'them Yanks canna' decide even whether to call their novel fabric Dacron or Terylene or what, so 'ow are they fit to tackle Hitler?'

She moaned with a faint far-away smile, sure now of victory.

'Tha's reduced to petty arguments, Alf. What's naming o' a man-made fibre compared wi' t'vast potential o' t'United States?' She moaned again as he tore away the last buttons and entered her, shy to be naked even now.

So Paul Kane was conceived. And afterwards as Alfred slept, Elsie wondered a little about the child she was sure she carried, about the impending crisis in the Middle East, about the true intentions of the United States and most of all, about the dark enigma of Soviet Foreign Policy.

Johnson's enthusiastic approval of this version was

clouded only by a doubt as to whether Elsie did not now win the argument a shade too quickly and completely. It was therefore agreed that Alf's point about income-tax levels should be expounded into a brief discussion of Britain's war-debts and generally doubtful post-war economic prospects, also that he would develop briefly but cogently his objections to "Song of Bernadette".

The matter of the suppression of the *Daily Worker* brought up the whole question of the Kane family's politics and it was quickly agreed that to avoid the inconvenient plot ramifications which might be entailed if either parent or both of them were to be Communists, ILP members or the like, that both of them would make it clear that they were approaching the question of the condition of Europe, and specifically of whether or not to seek the conception of the future Paul Kane that night, from an orthodox Labour Party point of view.

The Story Begins

Kipling was now ready to take the story of Paul Kane on into childhood.

> Paul first became aware that he was different from other children when he was about six, in the summer of 1948. His elder brother, Richard, who must have been nine or so, found himself one day with no 'big boys' of his own age to play with, so he was reduced to playing with Paul. He led Paul down to the beck.
>
> 'Yon beck's a river in China, river Yangtze like, sithee,' he said. The beck was about eight feet wide, almost dry and full of smooth stones, but to Paul it was big, a bit frightening and might well have rivalled the Yangtze for all he knew.
>
> 'Tha's t'Communist army. Have this stick and go across and shoot from ower t'Beck. I'll be t'other lot, that is, t'Kuomintang and shoot from ower 'ere, then I'll charge across and shoot thee. Think on tha's got to shout and scream right when I shoot thee.'
>
> 'Should we not 'ave negotiations first?' Paul qua-

vered. ''Appen get United Nations in . . .?'

'United Nations,' gritted Richard scornfully, 'Bloody United Nations, they've done no good in Palestine 'ave they, nor yon other place, Java? What bloody good's United Nations?'

'But they'll never succeed, like, if folk go about just shooting and that and give 'em no chance,' Paul retorted, close to tears.

'Get ower yon beck,' Richard growled, 'and hide well, think on, tha's supposed to be a peasant guerrilla force tha' knows.'

Paul crossed the Yangtze, fought and died as he was bid. But that day he sensed a contempt in Richard that was more than the ordinary scorn of a 'big lad' for a 'baby'. That contempt was to grow.

Johnson found this exchange, purportedly between children of respectively six and nine, to be rather unduly cerebral and possibly implausibly well-informed. More importantly, it was lacking in action. Kipling re-wrote as follows from the point where the children reach the stream.

'Yon's a river in China or somewhere,' said Richard, 'and tha's a baddy and I'm a goody and I'm chasing thee wi' my sword.' He had a formidable sword, the centre-pole of an old umbrella, all the ribs gone, but handle and ferrule still intact and he now struck Paul heavily across the back of his legs with it.

'Should we not see if we can talk things over?' whimpered Paul. Richard hit Paul again, harder, and the younger child started to scramble across the slippery stones of the beck. Paul's feet were soaked when he reached the other side and tears were mingling with blood from a cut over his eye where Richard had struck him with the ferrule of his umbrella-sword.

'I'll give thee talk things over,' hissed Richard, beating Paul over the head and shoulders with the umbrella-sword until he fell to the ground, whining.

'Stop yon grizzling,' he commanded, kicking Paul violently in the ribs and abdomen. 'Now I'll drown thee!' he expostulated, and flung Paul bodily into one of the deeper parts of the beck, a little pool some eighteen inches deep. Paul dragged himself out and fled, whimpering. His brother pelted him as he ran with a volley of big stones from the beck and with even more painful abuse. 'Bugger off tha' soft little bastard!' From that day on there was a coolness between Richard and Paul.

'Well,' was Johnson's response to this new version, 'first it's Bertrand Russell meets Freddie Ayer, now it's *Lord of the Flies*. Look I suggested a bit of action, not "Psycho". I like the umbrella though, keep the umbrella.'

'Anything else?' asked Kipling, rather sharply.

'Yes. Why make Paul such a little twerp? All he does is whine and grizzle and go on about negotiated settlements. He may be brainy, but he doesn't have to be totally wet, surely?'

'Yes, a good point. His sensitivity and intelligence rather than his pacifism are the main ideas. Perhaps he could strike back at Richard – hit him fairly painfully with a stone from the beck. On the knee. Then Richard might see him with a grudging respect. But the whole point is that Paul's very thoughtfulness and intellectual leanings *lose* him Richard's respect forever.'

'Well,' suggested Johnson, 'say Richard is going out one day to face this big gang of nasty kids, OK? And he finds that Paul won't back him up – in fact, Paul has secretly sawn up Richard's umbrella, because of his thoughtful pacifism. So – contempt for pansy Paul from butch Rich. right? Like Grace Kelly in "High Noon", a bit. Then Paul could sneak round the back of, er, something and zap the bad kids with his catapult but Richard never knows who did it like in "The Man Who Killed Liberty Vallance". So Paul's gutsy, but despised all the same.'

'Why would a six-year-old child of Paul's tempera-
ment possess a catapult?' asked Kipling with some
impatience.

I made them some tea.

'Perhaps we'd better skip the battle of the Yangtze
and just have him learn to read quicker than the other
kids, to show he's different.'

'Rather tame,' said Kipling.

'Yes. By the way, the dialect always sounds very OK.
How did you learn it? Off TV?'

'No, no. Television is utterly useless. In the typical so-
called Northern situation comedy one encounters alle-
ged nuclear families where the father does a good
imitation of Leeds, the mother does a fair Salford, the
children do Rotherham, Middlesbrough and Hull. It's
laughable. No, I got the general hang of it from a little
book called *Lern Thisen Yorkshire* and I find with an hour
or so of daily practice it comes quite easily. And of
course we always holiday up there every year for really
extensive practice.'

'Well it's pretty good, I'd say. But this isn't getting us
round, over or through Yangtze Incident, is it?'

'No.'

I made them some more tea.

A New Approach

'I think I've got an angle,' said Johnson after some time.
'It's the point that Paul K. is brainy, not that he's all that
pacifist, that's the point OK? Point two, he's supposed
to be growing up with the twentieth century, so
somehow we must hang on to the historical echoes etc.
Point three, close-knit narrative is not really our main
strength. So how about snapshots? He has these old
snapshots, photos all with dates, of himself at different
stages of growing up and each one starts off his
memories of some incident which has Tizer and Hovis,
and balaclavas and all *that* stuff.' (Here Johnson indicated emphatically Kipling's large card index of items

31

on working-class childhood) 'and he also shows himself getting brainier and more distanced from his little pals, only slowly – and also how it all unfolds against the looming backcloth of the nuclear age etc. If you pick dates when something was going on in history to go on the photos, it would all fit nicely.'

'It sounds like a very helpful idea. But what about the periods between the snapshots – or were you thinking there would be a continuous cover of pictures, two or three hundred of them? I really doubt . . .'

'Not really – more like about six. Six vignettes. Impressionistic. And for the bits in between just say, "so another two years rolled by" sort of thing.'

'It could be the answer,' said Kipling, 'it's certainly worth a try.'

Kipling at first had some difficulty in writing the account of how the snapshots of Paul's childhood came to be taken and in what circumstances he, Paul, came to be in possession of them at the age of thirty or so. By this time, however, he was learning that vital part of the storyteller's craft, that is, the paring to the bone of inessentials. Thus, he settled, artfully, for 'Paul could never quite remember how he came by the old photographs . . .'

. . . The first of them measured some three inches by four, probably taken on the old black box camera which Paul remembered being allowed to dismantle when he was ten, only to find to his disappointment that it was indeed just a box. And yet a black cardboard box had preserved the bones of the story of his early life as vividly and surely as Boswell preserved the life of Johnson. The earliest picture was dated on the back. 11 June 1943. It was over-exposed, and had obviously been taken in bright sunshine. Bright sunshine appropriate to the day that the Mediterranean islet of Pantelleria fell to the Allies, opening the way to Sicily, even though on that 11th day of June 1943 the little island itself was so shrouded in smoke and dust from the allied bombing, that the Dunkirk veterans of the British 1st Division who captured it hardly saw the sun. Most of them were regular soldiers. They were told to go, and they went – Pantelleria, Peru or Portugal – they went.

Rather more sense of historical direction was possibly being felt that same day in Hot Springs, Virginia, as the politicians, the fixers and the bureaucrats, the Conference men, signed the papers, posed for photographers and newsreel cameras and made little speeches in praise of the agreement on post-war relief they had just signed. Did they know that they had started to build the United Nations Organization? Did they care? Or was it only the soggy heat of a Virginia June that they recalled afterwards, blurred together with all the Quebecs, the Yaltas, the Bretton Woods, that made up their strange war of drafts and compromises?

Paul Kane was in his cot in that overlit photograph of 11 June 1943. His father must have carried the cot outside, knowing that the old box camera would hardly function in the dark interior of a miner's cottage. Or perhaps Paul had been ill, and 'fetched outside for the sunshine'? He looked neither well nor ill standing up in the cot, pudgily grasping two of the bars like a little zoo-born animal, and looking at the camera lens steadily, without any trace of emotion on the slightly blurred face. The camera had in fact focused on the bars of the cot so that the baby Paul's clothing was an indeterminate grey and the background, the backyard of 12 Alma Terrace was reduced to a haze of brick wall crossed by what might have been a washing line.

It was the child's face, and the eyes, to which the adult Paul's attention always returned when he looked at this picture. So calm, indifferent, looking not quite at the camera lens but rather through it. Was there already a hint of vision, of sensitivity, of inner strength and imagination in those calm eyes?

Was it fanciful to see the Paul Kane of 1943, seventeen months old, as having a faint fore-knowledge of the Paul that was to be? 'You have me caged now' that calm face seemed to say 'but you will not keep me here. Whether you or I wish it or not, I am not of this place. You are my parents but I am mine because of what I am. And what I am, you cannot know. A new world is being made at this moment, on the battlefield, in men's minds. It is still young, this new world, still unsteady on its feet as I am on mine but it is coming and when it comes, it will be my world not yours. It will set me free to be what I am!'

'I like the clothes-line, that's a good gritty touch,' said Johnson. 'But I should cool down that bit where the kid is thinking things. What does he grow up to be actually?'

'He goes to Oxford, as you know, then he becomes lecturer in English at a provincial university. I thought, provisionally, Bristol.'

'There you are then, not anti-Christ, but English Lecturer at Bristol – so why not come clean – just put something like "the child behind those solemn unblinking eyes seemed to know, even then in that sunlit backyard at 12 Alma Terrace in 1943, seemed to know in some uncanny way that one day he would join the English Department at the University of Bristol."'

'But surely' (Kipling's tone was brusque) 'an infant of eighteen months would sound quite bizarre, credited with such precise fore-knowledge?'

'OK. How about "seemed to know in some strange uncanny way that one day he would get a good job in higher education. In the private sector".'

A long and sometimes heated discussion followed, and it was agreed that provisionally at least, the difficulty would be skirted, by attributing to the infant Paul of the photograph no knowledge of the future whatsoever.

On a more positive note, Kipling and Johnson agreed

also that in the next snapshot the young Paul would be set more firmly into his local background, with perhaps only a glancing reference to world affairs, to form a good contrast with the at once epic and yet slightly dreamlike quality of the first snapshot. The draft read thus:

> The next picture was clearer, and more self-consciously 'composed'. It was dated 27 July, 1947. It was a happy picture, and Paul always smiled a little when he looked at it.
>
> The five year old Paul was standing in the same old backyard of 12 Alma Terrace. He was proudly holding a little toy barrow, the wheels of it coated with tar from the melting roads of that hot childhood summer. It contained Paul's treasures: an old Mickey-Mouse gas-mask, a gnarled piece of aluminium (part of a V-I, someone had earnestly assured him), his father's old ARP tinhat, several discarded ration books (different colours according to your age, Paul recalled) an empty Tizer bottle (how well Paul remembered the pop of a newly opened bottle of Tizer and the curiously shaped cork with the rubber band round it), a used-up dolly blue, the shoe of an old flat-iron, an old bakelite radio ('wireless' rather, thought Paul. Hilversum ... Athlone ... what a strange, selective introduction to geography that yellowing plastic dial had provided). And labels – labels from Blended chocolate, Robin and Woodbine cigarette packets, labels from bottles of California Syrup of Figs, Golden Syrup, Golden Eye Ointment, Fennings Fever Cure, Fennings Cooling Powders, Carters Little Liver Pills, Palmolive soap wrappers, Pelaw and Cherry Blossom boot-polish tins, Toni Home Perm packets. The barrow was also crammed with back numbers of *Radio Times*, *Beano* and *Dandy* as well as the *Golden Annual for 1938*, the *Boy's Own Paper Annual for 1925* and a dog-eared shoal of Enid Blyton's *Sunny Stories*.

Paul had learned to read very early and now read so unusually avidly that his father had said 'Tha'll read thy 'ead off at this rate,' jokingly, but perhaps with a touch of disquiet as if he sensed the first stirrings of the changes in Paul that would one day separate him from his son.

Young Paul, however, was all pride and happiness in the picture, holding the barrow, and wearing his best 'Low shoes', thick socks and short corduroy trousers, his best lumberjacket, flannel shirt and knitted balaclava under his proudest possession, a silvered leatherette helmet.

Thus in the confidence of his worldly possessions he stood, in his five-year-old strength – hardly aware that a mere week before, Dutch forces had renewed their attacks in Indonesia, and quite unaware of the impending dissolution of the Peasant Party of Rumania.

'Super,' enthused Johnson, 'he's a bit over-dressed for a hot July but never mind, they were very over-protective in those days – all those fever-cures and laxatives. So they probably did dress the poor little sods up like Captain Oates, rain or shine. Just one tiny thing.'

'Well?' asked Kipling.

'Well, you're the expert – but – *Sunny Stories*? Weren't they a bit, well, poofy? I remember one about this fairy that was in charge of putting the lucky leaf on four-leaved clovers. Well one day she overslept and got behind and wasn't fulfilling her norm, and the top fairy was really pissed off and said if she didn't get the lead out she'd be put into the dandelion clock department – no, really – the dandelion clock department was a sort of Gulag staffed by gnomes – maybe she thought there'd be sexual harassment. There's a point – can one sexually harass a fairy? Anyway this fairy's grizzling in a dell or somewhere and sobs out her saga to some passing newt or whatever and wow, you've guessed it, all the little animals help her to stick the leaves on double quick and she gets the Fairy Order of Lenin.'

'Why are you telling me all this?' asked Kipling mildly.

'Well, the thing is all the *Sunny Stories* are like that – a friend of mine did an M.Phil on them. That's how I came to read the cloverleaf fairy one – they're soppy to the *n*th degree. Would Paul want to read such stuff?'

'I think it quite likely that his tastes, at five, would not be clearly formed and he would read anything – sauce-bottle labels, anything.'

'But what about his dad's attitude? What if his dad caught Paul with one? Hey, how about that? Dad finds sensitive Paul sobbing about the plight of some deprived elf in *Sunny Stories* – reads said story, tells Paul not to be a silly little sod. More sobs. First clash with dad. Early sign that Paul's not like other kids etc. It's a lot better introduction to the idea that Paul's very sensitive etc., than having him mugged by that psychopathic brother in the Yangtze.'

Kipling thought that the idea had great merit. He expanded the episode accordingly, after some difficult but necessary research to find a *Sunny Story* which would have sufficient power to interest and move young Paul to the point of tears, and yet not have literary or emotional interest enough to command the sympathetic attention of a rough but thoughtful coal miner. He was then ready for the third snapshot.

The third snapshot was much smaller, and had not been taken on the old box camera. It was an official school photograph, dated 16 October 1949. The end of the Greek Civil War had obviously troubled young Paul less than the problem of what expression to wear in the photograph. Already a self-conscious, sensitive child he had settled for a small friendly smile, which under the cameraman's bright flash had come out as a knowing leer. It was the check lumberjacket that stirred Paul's memory rather than his own long-ago face. The check lumberjacket meant Class 2, Class 2 meant Miss Baker.

Miss Baker had a gold tooth. She also had frizzy grey hair, like wire-wool, steel-rimmed spectacles, and wore thick grey stockings. She was crisp, strict. She did not talk posh like some of the younger teachers, but her speech showed that she definitely did not 'come frae rahnd here'. Her accent, Paul realized many years later, was a light East Lancashire, probably of the lower Colne Valley, but in 1949 it was just one more faintly unsettling fact about Miss Baker, along with her gold tooth and wire-wool hair. Miss Baker was a person not to tolerate being 'mucked about'.

She was efficient. She cared. She was not of outstanding intelligence but she could recognize unusual talent in others and she recognized it in Paul.

He was not always made happier by the recognition. Back in September she had written up the name ADENAUER on the blackboard, and asked if anyone knew how to say the odd, foreign name. Paul knew. He'd heard it on the wireless. He put his hand up, but for what felt like ages, Miss Baker ignored him, and asked other children to try to say it 'Andy ran' 'adune' 'around', the versions grew more and more desperate and unlikely. Finally she asked Paul. 'Adenauer,' he said clearly, with the Westphalian inflection learned from BBC newsreaders. She looked at him sharply. 'Very good, Paul Kane,' she said, 'say it again'. She made him say it five times altogether. Loudly. 'There!' she cried, 'if Paul can pronounce correctly the name of the newly elected Chancellor of West Germany, there's no reason why any child in this class of normal IQ and reasonable level of motivation should not do the same.' Paul could feel his ears turning red.

Despite his Adenauer triumph, however, Paul was both amazed and frightened when Miss Baker presented herself on the doorstep of 12 Alma Terrace one autumn evening in 1949. Paul had answered the knock. 'Hello Paul, are your mam and dad at home?'

she enquired, 'Aye, they're 'avin' their tea,' gasped Paul. Miss Baker came in, and addressing both Mr and Mrs Kane, said, 'I feel I must tell you something of moment about Paul.' 'Tha's never going to tell us tha's dissatisfied wi' t' lad's scholastic progress?' frowned Alfred. 'Nor please God, that tha's owt to complain of wi'reference to 'is general conduct and integration into 'is peer group?' chimed in Elsie, anxiously. 'Quite the contrary,' averred Miss Baker. 'He is a boy of outstanding ability and promise.'

'Oh, champion,' beamed Alfred. 'Ay, champion,' smiled Elsie.

'And that's as far as I've got,' said Kipling. 'I'm stuck. I don't know why she's come'.

I made them some tea.

'What if she's come to the wrong house by mistake,' Johnson ventured. 'Or what if, hey, I like this, Miss Baker is in love with Paul's dad? What if she makes up any excuse to come and see him, just to be near his manly thews? No? Say she's in love with Paul then – spring and autumn? Only trying to help.'

Kipling made no verbal reply to these suggestions but removed his glasses and closed his eyes and rubbed the bridge of his nose. Even I could sense the air of creative crisis, as he glowered morosely at Johnson. Johnson stirred his tea with a spoon, tink, tink. Irritatingly.

'Have you tried the old Plan B, making a list of the kind of things teachers do and say when they come to see parents in books. Like you did with the conception scene – rather brilliantly, I thought?'

'I did try. The trouble is, teachers in literature rarely go to see parents at all and when they do –' he handed Johnson a sheet of paper headed 'Teachers (visiting parents) (at home)'. It read '1. break news of child's expulsion from school for (a) theft, (b) cheating. 2. Request parent(s) to stop beating child, starving child, sending child to tend cows.'

'Not very helpful really is it?' said Kipling sourly.

'Well, we could follow up the tending cows angle, perhaps. Could Paul be kept at home by his father who ruthlessly makes him tend the flock of prize pigeons. He has to exercise the pigeons all the time and he's so tired at school he falls asleep over his books?'

I made some more tea.

'What you've got to do,' said Johnson, 'is learn how to do plot, and also polish up dialogue while we're at it. So shelve, as it were, Miss Baker for now. Practice on easy plot and easy dialogue. Try kids. All they do is have dorm-feeds and climb trees and play doctors and nurses etc. And what sort of stuff do they say? All they say is stuff like "Yah, leggo you rotters". So start easy, with kids. See yourself as a sort of apprentice.'

'But you will recall I had child-to-child dialogue in the Yangtze incident as you call it, and that turned out less than well.'

'Yes, yes, but you were trying to plug messages in that bit about brotherly love (lack of), how Paul first realized he was weird etc. What I've got in mind is straight kid-stuff narrative and kid-talk. How about a bit of vandalism? Paul is a bit of a little stuffed shirt, so far isn't he? Do some vandalism, no overtones, nor under-tones, just chucking bricks through old ladies' windows and running away. There's acres of stuff like that in books, *Just William*, e.g. That film with public schoolboys where they get a bren-gun on a roof. Hey, here's a free idea. This latest snapshot of Paul is taken in October 1949 right? so it reminds grown up Paul of how the kids collected wood and stuff for a November 5th-type bonfire, and you can top it off with a nice atmospheric bit about Bonfire Night, with flickering firelight and bangs etc., such as you're good at. But remember – plot and dialogue!'

Apprentice Days (1)

Kipling's reluctant early efforts to submit himself to this new discipline were deemed promising by Johnson.

This very first effort was criticized on only one score:

'It's October, Paul, time we initiated t' traditional Guy Fawkes wood-gatherin' or progging,' averred Paul's friend, Eric, one opalescent autumn evening in 1949. 'By eck, tha's right,' Paul concurred. So they collected a large pile of wood, and at the appropriate hour on November 5th 1949, set fire to it.

'Great,' was Johnson's cheerful and encouraging comment. 'But a shade, well, short. Get some more characters in and specify stuff like types and sources of wood and how obtained.'
'Where would they get wood, actually?' asked Kipling, a touch plaintively. 'The area is virtually treeless.'
'Well, where did you get wood for Bonfire Night when you were a kid?'
'I think actually in St Albans, the local authority arranged the fires and fireworks. I'll put in some research, though.'
His research was vigorous and fruitful.

They gathered after tea on that opalescent October evening at the end of the street, the Alma Terrace gang, chewing their sticks of liquorice though some of them favoured the commercial liquorice compound known as 'Spanish', passing the bottle of dandelion and burdock from hand to grubby hand. Eric was the acknowledged leader. 'Plot Night soon, sithee, Proggin' time according to long-standing tradition,' he announced gruffly. 'Where shall we get wood?' asked Paul. 'Pinch it, clart-head,' sneered Tony. 'Wait till t'Park Crescent lot have built their fire and then pinch t'lot, night before Plot night.' 'Great!' gritted Jack and some of the others. 'But think on,' doubted Paul, 'if t'plan fails, then we'll have nowt to show. Yon's a high-return but high-risk sort of plan.' 'Let's go down Scott's yard and pinch 'is timber,' suggested Granville. 'It's thieving but we're under age as yet for full criminal proceedings like, we'd nobbut get a supervision order, worst way up, and they'd 'ev ter catch us first.'

So it was agreed, as a first move, that the yard of Scott, the timber merchant, should be raided and a satisfactory core of 4 × 2 and other timber was secured on the night of 17 October from that source.

'What about t'railway yard? They've sleepers and such,' suggested Harry at the next gang meeting. 'Ay,' opined Eric. 'They're nationalized now, so its property o't community by rights, so we can tek it.' 'Surely,' interposed Paul, 'we're only a part o't community and if we nick stuff off t'railway we're pinchin' from t'community and so in a way robbin' oursen?'

'Shurrup,' cried Eric, Tony, Granville, Harry and others in unison.

So it came about that on successive nights, sleepers, and pit-props and also a quantity of pitch and train oil were with some difficulty manhandled over the wall surrounding the railway yard, and placed on the fire-to-be.

Eric's ambition grew with the growing pile of wood at the end of Alma Terrace. 'We'll go up Rose Avenue, up to t'posh 'ouses, and 'ave front gates off their 'inges, when it's dark,' he declared. 'Yes, that could be seen sithee, as a form of clear expropriation of one class by another, not just pinchin',' opined Paul. So the garden gates of Rose Avenue, Myrtle Walk and other lower middle-class streets joined the growing pyre. Len and Terry, the most manually skilful of the gang, prised off the house names and numbers, where necessary, to avert detection.

'What about some of them trees in t' park,' suggested Lance on 28 October. 'Too hard,' objected Matthew. 'Nay there's nowt to it,' rejoined Clive. 'There is an' all,' retorted Wilfred. 'Shurrup,' growled Brian. 'I'll bash thee!' threatened Gavin. Some order was restored by Eric and it was decided that the park's trees would indeed be raided the next evening. Frank had 'borrowed' a big saw from his father, a pit carpenter, and the trees were, therefore, dealt with surprisingly quickly.

A fire of respectable size was thus ready on the corner of Alma Terrace and Inkerman Road by November 5th awaiting only the Guy itself, which the twins Alan and Stephen made out of sacks and an old army greatcoat. 'It's not so bad eh?' said Eric, proudly surveying the pile as the match was applied. 'Tha's a gift for under statement, tha' knows, Eric,' said Clive, the sycophant of the group. But even Clive's 'creeping' for once could not spoil the gang's pleasure as, clutching their liquorice sticks and bottles of dandelion and burdock, they gleefully watched the flames take hold. The smell of burning timber, the feel of the round swell of a toffee-apple . . .

'Hold it,' Johnson almost shouted. 'Sod toffee-apples! Hold it . . . I've got to think!'

He had never before interrupted Kipling in full flow and was clearly agitated.

'Could you make the gang bigger? Like two or three hundred?'

'Well,' said Kipling, taken aback. 'Wilson and Rowley in *Growing up in an Industrial Microcosm* are quite specific. They say that street-based juvenile, that is, sub-teen, gangs in northern mining communities of the '40s and '50s ranged in size from six members to twenty, partly according to the size of street, of course, but also, interestingly, related to the thickness of the local coal seams. Postulating Alma Terrace as a longish street and the local seams as reasonably thick, that gave me eighteen as a fair number – perhaps rather large for much characterization of individuals . . .'

'Do you realize you've written stuff that is potentially intensely visually exciting?'

'The fire, you mean?'

'No, no – pinching the wood! Imagine. A mob of kids, crawling over that timberyard, like ants and a long line of them all carrying logs and stuff, all the way up the hill to Alma Terrace by the light of flickering torches. Its Eisenstein, man! With Prokofiev-type doomy music. And old man Scott left alone in the timber yard, sobbing. Clutching a handful of sawdust. All that's left to him. Trampled to death. Sobbing first and then trampled to death. But you can't storm the winter timber yard with eighteen kids. We'll need hundreds for the panoramic effect. We could tight focus on Paul, then pull slowly back, like the good bit in "Gone With The Wind" with all those wounded blokes in the railway station – you pull back and see that there's dozens, scores, *hundreds* of the little bastards all hauling off big chunks of four by two, all horrible and gleeful.'

'But plausibility? Wilson's and Rowley's evidence?'

'Sod Wilson and Rowley! We're talking about a cinematic experience. Most people who go to the pictures weren't even born in 1949. South Yorks in 1949 – you could put Aztec temples and Tarzan up there they wouldn't know any better, ignorant berks. No, all people want is a good film. You had thought about the film rights I assume?'

'Well, not a great deal, not in detail I mean,' confessed Kipling, defensively.

'So start thinking now. Look, we don't need to settle details today like how many kids in the gang. It could be eighteen in the book and five hundred in the film, people don't notice stuff like that anyway. Just write your own thing but start to think in visual-values terms. Dammit, we're half-way there already come to think – the conception scene is a visual natural, there's cameo parts already written for big stars to do Wavell and Hitler and everybody, we could use cheap grainy old newsreels for all the history bits, the whole childhood bit is based on photographs already. We're a genius! Also in films instead of dialogue people can just look meaningfully and things. And if we got some big name Frog director, or something, people won't care if they can't follow the plot. They'll just think it's supposed to be like that.'

'I am writing a novel,' said Kipling firmly, 'the story is a possibly inept but sincere attempt to explore the life and mind of someone who is an exact contemporary of mine, but whose experience has been utterly different from my own – that's why I sent him to Oxford when I myself went to Cambridge, for instance. If it makes a film some day, well and good, but I really must not be diverted by these intrusive considerations from a different medium.'

'Right,' said Johnson. 'A novel. And a cracker – with, among other things a very powerful visual element?'

'Yes. Well I could certainly look at the whole thing again, from the angle of striking visual images, colours and the like. That could be very useful indeed in its own right. Thank you.'

Apprentice Days (2)

A Fresh Start from a New Angle

Some of the material Kipling had already written lent itself very readily to the new visual approach. The Wavell, Halder and Pegram scenes, for instance, needed only the addition of more specific references to the colours and shapes of items of office furniture, uniforms and the like.

Few purely literary problems were met in the re-writing of the rest of the material, though much wearisome research was needed before Kipling could specify the colours of all the objects, especially the numerous labels, in little Paul's wheelbarrow load of treasures in snapshot number two.

Somewhat more difficulty was met when Kipling began to write new material with the 'visual angle', as it were, in mind from the start.

He began with a tender evocation of Paul's first love, through further reference to 'Snapshot' number three:

Autumn 1949 and Class 2 meant more than Guy Fawkes night adventures with the Alma Terrace gang. It meant Betty Shackleton, Paul's first love . . . . She was a slightly built child, a full inch shorter than Paul. Her hair was best described as a dark blonde, cut severely but to Paul's eyes fetchingly, in a fringe which came down to within some half an inch of her well-shaped light brown eyebrows. Her face was fresh coloured. Her nose was somewhat snub, and featured some dozen tiny freckles rather more of them on the left of the nose than on the right. Her eyes were grey-blue inclining to roundness. The mouth was rather small, which perhaps contributed to a general impression of pertness. Her teeth had the whiteness of childhood and one of them on the front left hand side of her lower jaw was somewhat set back from correct alignment with the others, though not so markedly as to call for a brace.

She wore a selection of often rather grubby knee-length frocks. Paul particularly recalled a mustard-yellow one, ruched at the front, with elbow length sleeves, patterned at the hem and cuffs with dark blue.

He remembered vividly also a dark pink frock, patterned with small white daisy-like flowers, with puffed, short sleeves and a slightly uneven hemline. Betty always wore cardigans to school, whatever the weather. One featured two large slanted pockets, three large buttons and was cable-knitted in the shade then innocently known as 'Nigger Brown'. The pale blue one had only one shallow pocket, on the right, and was in Paul's opinion much more becoming, though it was marred somewhat by two small but obstinate black ink-stains, one on the left cuff, one near the second of the four white buttons.

At 'hometime', Betty wore in cold weather a light brown double-breasted coat, cut a shade skimpily, with slanting side pockets and velveteen collar and cuffs and six large cloth covered buttons. Her knee-length socks were normally plain white but sometimes she wore light-brown socks with dark brown clocks of floral design. In summer she wore scuffed patent-leather black shoes, with a single strap-over button fastening and in winter sturdier tan-coloured brown 'lace-ups' with a light brogue effect of punched holes. In wet weather of course muddy black Wellington boots were favoured.

'This is a girl or a mobile jumble-sale?' Johnson asked, rhetorically and unhelpfully when he read this passage.

'Visual values, emphasis on, I suggested. And what does he write me, a Littlewood's catalogue! What is this kid Paul anyway, a clothes fetishist? Hey, wait a minute – how about that? He could be, you know, a juvenile transvestite?'

'She doesn't wear these things all at once as I thought I'd made clear in the text,' said Kipling.

'Constructively,' continued Kipling, firmly ignoring Johnson's interesting transvestism idea, 'what do you suggest?'

'OK, Scrub transvestism. Dress Betty up in just one of her outfits. Just one, right? Describe it, OK, then make some plot happen and some dialogue for God's sake and mix the visual in with the plot and dialogue in an integrated way.'

'I'll try,' said Kipling, with a small sigh, and re-wrote the episode quite radically, as follows:

'I like them little daisy things on yon dark pink frock o'thine,' said Paul boldly, one playtime. 'Nay 'ey up, sithee,' blushed Betty, but she smiled nonetheless showing her enchantingly misaligned little white lower tooth. 'What about t'cardigan then?' she queried coyly, wrinkling her snub nose and drawing attention thereby to the dozen or so unevenly distributed freckles on or about it. 'Don't like it much. Never did care for yon nigger brown 'un,' said Paul with the dreadful and uncalculated frankness of childhood. This caused Betty to knit her well-shaped dark eyebrows in a scowl and toss, insofar as one can toss rather severely cut hair, her dark blonde hair.

Paul felt an urgent need to re-establish himself in her eyes. 'I'm off ter't pictures, Sat'day. Going to see "T' Mummy's Curse".' Her rather round grey-blue eyes widened. 'But yon's in't newly introduced censorship category o' picture known as "H" so they'll not let thee in on account of thee being under age.' 'I'll gerrin,' bragged Paul. 'Well,' said Betty, 'think on if tha' does to give us an accurate outline o' t'no doubt grisly plot. Roger Knowles is going to try and gerrin and see it, he says and he said he'd tell us all about it. But you can tell us i'stead,' she continued shyly, 'if tha's a mind, sithee, na' then, ey up', And so the interview was concluded.

Paul was in fact unable to gain admittance to 'The Mummy's Curse'. The two adults he tentatively approached, begging them to 'Tek us in mister,' told him respectively to 'Bugger off' and 'Sod off'. However there were six quite vivid pictures of episodes in the film in a frame outside the cinema, stills from which a creatively gifted child such as Paul could easily construct a plausibly horrific sounding outline of a plot. Also, he felt sure that Roger Knowles would not be able to see the film either, so it was with fair confidence that he approached Betty the following Monday and began to recount his concocted outline of the plot of 'The Mummy's Curse'.

He found, however, that somehow his ingrained intellectual honesty would not let him look her in the eye. He fixed his gaze instead on her black patent leather, single strap shoes and white knee length socks, 'and that's how it ended,' he concluded. 'Tha's not said about yon big snake!' interrupted, from behind Paul, the harsh yet oily voice of Roger Knowles. 'Oh, yes,' quavered Paul, 'there was a right big snake, a reticulated or Indian python, as it were, and, er . . .' 'No, there was no such thing,' gritted Knowles, triumphantly. 'A bloke took me in, as a result o' persistent and importunate requests o' my part, but evidently tha' couldn't gain admission, Paul Kane, else tha'd know there weren't no snake reticulated nor otherwise.'

Paul was totally at a loss. 'Fibber,' spat Betty, 'tha's made up fibs just to gain credit and try to mek out tha's socially adept and skilful at gerrin' inter 'orrifying "H" pictures. Tha's nobbut a fibber sithee.' She turned on her heel. The brown cardigan disappeared in the throng of children. Paul never saw her again.

'Why not?' asked Johnson in challenging tones, 'she's in the same bloody class as wee Paul so why does he never see her again? Where did she go? What have you done with her? You're not going to drop a gargoyle on her, are you?'

'All right, your point is taken. I'll simply amend it to the effect that things were somehow never the same again between Betty and Paul.'

'Good. And that apart, it's fine. Really, starts to feel like going places – Honest.'

'Well, I did have an alternative version roughed out, actually, in which Paul goes to see some quite accessible, non "H" film on the Saturday and tells Betty the plot, on the Monday. I thought that might give me some practice in at least recounting, if not devising, plots. I thought "Bicycle Thieves" or possibly "Fallen Idol" might be suitable.'

'She could go and see it herself,' said Johnson, with ruthless logic. 'Unless she was blind. Or deaf. Hey! How about this Betty being deaf and blind and Paul has to tell her everything that's going on in Braille or something. Only he makes it all up to be more exciting and interesting than it really is, like there's a new kid comes to school with gold clogs, or the new teacher turns out to be Margaret Lockwood in disguise. Or Hitler, OK? Then one day she finds out the boring truth from this little Roger Knowles bastard who learns Braille to tell her out of pure malice. And she hates Paul ever after?'

'It's interesting, but I don't think such a severely

handicapped child would have been admitted to an ordinary state primary school, not in 1949.'

'OK, leave it as it is. Scrub blind. But with regret.'

So it was agreed, though the central idea of physical handicap was to bear fruit thereafter.

'I feel ready now for more complex plot situations, I think,' said Kipling, a few days later. 'I'd also like to involve adults now and experiment with more demanding dialogue. Also I think I've got the answer on Miss Baker's visit to the Kanes.'

'Great – just remember the visual angles,' was Johnson's only comment. This was the new episode in its draft form:

Paul could never forget his final summer weeks in Miss Baker's Class 2. He recalled most vividly the heat-shimmering afternoon of 27 June, 1950. They were doing long division. Paul glanced up at the tall classroom window noting for the thousandth time the slightly chipped cream-coloured paint of the window-frame. There was a face at the window . . . Paul knew that face, knew the intelligent but shifty eyes, the wicked but disarming grin, the grey stubble of whiskers at the chin. He knew the face all right, and felt a mixture of surprise, some pleasure, mostly fear at the thought of the embarrassment which might lie only a minute or two ahead, of what Miss Baker might say, if . . .

'Go away,' he mouthed silently at the face, and was thankful when it suddenly disappeared. Relief, however, was replaced within seconds by a complex mixture of puzzlement, curiosity, anger, disbelief, happiness and dismay as not only Rex's face but the whole dog bounded into the classroom. Rex, a fox-terrier cross, largely white except for both ears and some ninety per cent of his face which were black, turning grey in the chin area and a similar proportion of his tail which was dark brown, rushed straight to Paul, leaped onto his brown, ink-stained desk and

50

began to lick Paul's face furiously, at the same time whining with evident pleasure and urgently pawing the boy's chest.

'Who owns this dog?' asked Miss Baker sternly.

'Paul Kane,' leered the detestable Roger Knowles, grinning.

'How do you know, Roger Knowles?' queried Miss Baker grimly.

'Miss, if tha'all tek trouble to examine t'collar o' yon dog, tha'll see t'words 'Kane, 12 Alma Terrace' engraved on t'small brass medal attached thereto,' said Roger smugly. 'Also, t'dog's plainly singled out Paul Kane for special attention sithee, by gum.'

'What is the meaning of this, Paul Kane?' cried Miss Baker crossly.

'Nay Miss,' stammered Paul, 'that question were really best addressed to t'beast 'isself. I can mysen but speculate as to 'is motives for bustin' in 'ere so untimely like.'

'Paul Kane's a fibber, Miss,' spitefully and unnecessarily put in Betty Shackleton.

'Shurrup fibber thisen!' rejoined Freda Mitchell, a girl who favoured emerald green cardigans and brown shoes and entertained a childish passion for Paul, which he unhappily could not return because of his slight but definite aversion to Freda's red-haired pale skinned, physical type, well though he liked Freda as a person.

'Silence Class 2!' gritted Miss Baker. 'Let Paul himself give us his account, or theory at least as to this creature's motives in intruding in such an unseemly fashion.'

'Nay, by gum,' croaked Paul feebly, completely at a loss for explanation or excuse. Rex whined furiously.

Then inspiration flashed.

'Rex!' cried Paul. 'I'm off to ask thee some questions, put in such a fashion, does't see, that a simple "Ay" or "Nay" will be appropriate answers. If tha' means "Ay" bark once, if 'tis "Nay", sithee, bark twice!' Rex sat obedient and attentive on Paul's desk. Roger Knowles sniggered.

'Now then, Rex, what brings thee here – does tha' wish to warn us all about some bad turn i't' Far Eastern situation?' (This was but two days after the outbreak of the Korean War and the entire world shared Paul's concern on this matter. Millions who had never heard of Korea, millions who had never dreamed that that remote peninsula could ever touch their lives now paced the floor beside radio sets waiting for crumbs of news.) Rex barked. Twice. Paul felt both relief and frustration.

'Is there 'appen news of a new government in France to replace that of Mr Bidault?' Two barks. 'Is it summat nearer home, by gum?' One sharp bark. The silence and tension in the room were palpable. No sniggers now. 'Is it my dad?' One bark. Sinking dread. 'Ast' been a roof-fall, explosion, or summat, at pit?' One bark. Paul's eyes filled with tears. 'Is he, is he . . .?' he quavered. Rex shook his head and barked twice, emphatically and Paul felt the shadow move away.

'Is he 'appen injured, been taken 'ome, and me mam's that distraught she knows not rightly what to do, like, and you instinctively felt that tha' should come and get me, sithee?' One single, triumphant bark.

Pausing only to secure the necessary permission of Miss Baker, and to leave an explanatory note for brother Richard (in Class 4) with the school secretary, Paul ran home, Rex at his heels, up Arkwright Street, past the 'Royal Oak', its doors and window frames still painted a pre-war, glum maroon shade, the words 'Snug' and 'Saloon' picked out in flaking silver gilt on the windows, down Inkerman Street and along the familiar cobbles of Alma Terrace to number 12.

He flung open the front door still trim and shiny in a month old coat of olive green paint.

'Thank God tha's come,' cried his mother. 'Nay, it

were no trouble,' replied Paul, soothingly. 'Nay lad,' his father croaked feebly, 't'is good to see thee.'

His father was lying on the settee, his head supported by a green cushion, covered in appliqué work showing an eighteenth century lady in a crinoline watering a flowerbed with a watering can.

'T' were nobbut a bit of a roof fall. T'lads had me out in a trice but t'owld legs bust, I doubt,' he indicated his heavily strapped and splinted left leg. 'All's well now, lad, sithee but thy mam'll be right glad o' thy prompt emotional support, so enterprisingly secured by yon little 'un.' He indicated Rex, who was clearly basking in this flood of unusually total and universal approval.

An hour later, Paul was amazed and not a little nervous to find Miss Baker, dressed in a light grey two-piece costume over a beige turtle-neck sweater on the doorstep. 'Come in Miss,' he quavered, doubtfully.

'I have come,' she announced to the Kanes, 'with three purposes in mind. Firstly to give you this, Mr Kane, with best wishes for your speedy recovery.' She brought out from a brown carrier bag a pound box of Black Magic chocolates with a bright red tassel attached to it. 'Nay, nay, lass, 'ole pound boxes o' Black Magic be not for t'like o'colliers,' protested Alfred. 'Now now, Mr. Kane, this is 1950, we'll have no such talk,' said Miss Baker firmly. 'The future of this country may not be so entirely and firmly in the hands of the organized working class as appeared in the heady days of 1945, but the economic and political gains of the first Attlee administration will not be lightly lost and there is no longer any room for archaic social attitudes such as you have just given voice to.'

'Ay, by gum, well I never,' cried Elsie. 'Tha's reet there tha' knows. Thy analysis is simple, but profound, sithee.'

'Secondly,' went on Miss Baker, 'I came to congratulate you on your possession of such an intelligent small dog.'

Rex hung his head sheepishly and would have blushed had he been physiologically capable of doing so.

'Thirdly it seems to me an appropriate moment to tell you something which I, at least, deem important, about Paul, here.' 'Ee, nowt bad, nowt to t'lad's discredit, and by implication, therefore, to ours?' cried Elsie, nervously rubbing her hands down her dark green single-pocketed pinny. 'Quite otherwise. He is a boy of outstanding intelligence, sensitivity and insight and particularly good at Composition. I thought you should know.'

As Elsie and Alf muttered their inarticulate thanks and offered Miss Baker tea, which was refused with great tact and politeness, Paul boldly asked, 'One thing still puzzles me, Miss Baker, 'ow did Rex who reaches barely eighteen inches when stood up on 'is back legs at full stretch, manage to look through t'classroom window which mun be five feet off t'ground at least?'

Miss Baker smiled, the first time Paul remembered her smiling since the February election had come so close to unseating the Labour Government. 'I wondered when you would ask that. I investigated that very matter straight after school. Beneath the window in question I found a pile of big cardboard boxes formerly containing tins of peas and the like. These, Rex must have dragged from somewhere near the school dustbins.' 'Thus forming,' cried Paul excitedly, 'a rickety but adequate platform –' 'For a small, light dog –' said Miss Baker, 'to press 'is nose agin t'winder,' triumphantly concluded Paul.

'Quite so,' agreed Miss Baker crisply and strode off down Alma Terrace in her flat-heeled light tan brogues.

'Terrific. Really,' was Johnson's comment. 'But where

the hell is Richard?' 'Richard?' echoed Kipling, some-what blankly. 'Ah yes, brother Richard.'

'He is, perhaps, playing truant but for the best of motives,' suggested Kipling. 'He is out looking for the family's other dog, Prince, who could be, say, a black and white collie, prone to stray. He finds Prince, returns with him, circa 6 o'clock and the contrast between his un-punitive but relatively cool reception and the adulation of Paul and Rex envenoms the relationship between the boys as you suggested. It also envenoms the relationship of the two dogs – the dogs' rivalry and progressive alienation from each other could reflect and echo that of the two boys. A sort of counterpoint.'

'Bingo!' cried Johnson, in slightly surprised admiration and approval. 'First prize for the fat lady in the blue hat. This is getting easy, isn't it?'

'Easier,' said Kipling cautiously.

That same evening, Kipling who had worked at unusual speed produced a draft for the outline of the next episode, based on 'snapshot' number four, a family seaside group photograph dated 'Filey, 1 August, 1952'. The snap was to feature Mr and Mrs Kane in deckchairs, smiling. Richard and Paul would be sitting together on the sand, to all appearances amicably, but a keen observer would see that Richard has just slyly elbowed Paul in the kidney region, and Paul's smile is actually a rictus of pain. In the foreground, Rex and Prince are lying facing each other, with outwardly friendly doggy grins, but a close examination of the hindquarters of each dog would show that they were in fact tensed, about to spring at each other's throats.

The plot outline involved a dog-fight, followed by a fist fight (i.e. Paul v. Richard). Paul fled into the sea to escape. Paul in danger of drowning. Rescued by Prince (symbolic of incipient reconciliation, also the rescue of a large child by a fox-terrier would be less plausible than such a rescue by a collie). Later Richard would be buried by a fall of sand from a dune, then dug out by Rex. Temporary, at least, reconciliation of Rex, Richard,

Paul and Prince would then follow. The terrier's innate propensity to dig would give the sand-dune episode total credibility.

'Could I have a minute to think about this?' asked Johnson. He wrote rapidly for a few minutes and then read out the following:

The Whoever Sanction

Bunch of important whoevers. Sky-jacked by PLO. But whoevers turn out to be girl SAS types in disguise. Long hi-jack bit, tension, endless cups of coffee deadlines, sweaty faces, clocks (ticking) etc. Then SAS girls fling aside disguises and zap PLO types with concealed guns. But leader of SAS girls by now in love with leader of PLO types – both flee, pursued by hitmen from both sides, to Switzerland, Amsterdam, Japan, and other scenic places. Etc.

'What does this mean?' asked Kipling reasonably. 'What are a group of, er, whoevers, disguised or otherwise, doing on the beach at Filey? And what is a "sanction" in this context?'

'Sanction means – well they call this sort of thing Sanction and Mandate and Protocol, it doesn't mean anything. It's just to show it's a thriller. And that's what you should be writing before you go any further. I know what you're going to say – but look at the facts – look at all those people you knocked off in those early drafts, and remember the Yangtze? And you were going to do away with poor little Betty Shackleton if I'd let you, and now look – rabid dogs running amok, fist-fights, dune-disasters. Look, if you're writing to sublimate violent instincts, OK. Who's ashamed? But do it. Get it out of your system. Get some loot out of it too. Royalties – heard of them? You could get a proper electric typewriter, with the Whoever Sanction money. Then, Shazzam! Back to Paul Kane. You can do the Whoever Sanction under another name, I won't tell anybody.'

'I appreciate what you are trying to do. And certainly

the true motives of any author are doubtless always mixed and open to question. I read somewhere that *Madame Bovary* was written as an act of expiation, or for a bet or something of that kind, and it may well be that I am, at some unconscious level, trying somehow to, what's the word, sublimate violent instincts. But in this particular case, the Filey beach scene I mean, I think I was merely led astray a little, perhaps, by my interest in the new factor represented by the dogs and their relationship and neither my research nor unaided imagination could come up with much for a pair of dogs to dŏ, actually, except – well, look for yourself.' Kipling consulted his card-index on pairs of dogs in literature. 'See. In literature they fight (sixty per cent of references) rescue people from drowning (twenty per cent), dig people out of sand, earth, collapsed buildings (fourteen per cent). The only other thing any dogs do at all, let alone pairs of dogs, is come home from long distances, howl over graves, growl at ghosts and pursue foxes, otters and the like. None of which seemed to me very germane to Paul's story. Unless Richard died of course. Then they could howl over his grave. Or Prince could. Perhaps Rex would not wish to.'

'There you go again. Knocking people off. If you'd written *War and Peace* it would have finished up as *Robinson Crusoe.*'

'Yes, yes, that was not a totally serious suggestion. Look I give my word to restrain this tendency to destroy my characters if you promise to forget the Whoever Sanction.'

'OK. Deal. Perhaps we're all a bit tired.'

I made them some tea.

'I like the seaside idea though. Send them to the seaside but leave the dogs at home,' said Johnson.

'Who would feed the dogs?'

'Chrissake! Details, details! Let the dogs catch horrible Roger Knowles. Nobody'll miss him. They drag his body back to 12 Alma Terrace and eat him. He should last them a week if they're careful.'

'I think the neighbours could probably feed the dogs.'

'OK. Now, the *famille* Kane are all at the seaside, dogless. So what happens? Thinks. What's happened to Paul so far? Turned down by his girl, but victorious pronouncer of Adenauer and co-planner of the great wood robbery, and now this latest triumph with help of Rex the dog. I make that three triumphs to one humiliation, so he's due a humiliation. Also, we need more action from Dad, I think. He had a featured role in the conception bit, and lay on the sofa with his leg splinted in the dog bit, but really he hasn't as it were yet taken the actual stage in a vertical condition, has he?'

'So,' summarized Kipling, 'I need a plot line involving Paul's father and, of course, dialogue and colours and other visual references.'

'Also while you're at it, see if you can't, you know, knit the twentieth-century history stuff into the action a bit more sort of closely, make it sort of impinge.'

'It's a challenge. But I'll certainly do my best. This is really very helpful, thank you.' And so Kipling set to work. The draft was ready for Johnson's attention in a few days:

Everybody in the seaside snap dated Scarborough Aug. 1st 1952 looked unusually happy. Alfred Kane had the fierce grin of a soldier or an athlete, perhaps, who had come through, triumphed in some ordeal. Elsie's smile was that of someone who has just been struck by a happy inspiration, or some total and uncomplicated answer to a vexing, long-standing problem.

Richard's was a smile of the eyes rather than the lips, the smile of someone welcoming, a little shyly, a friend who has been long away. Paul's smile was more confiding, like that of someone sharing a joke or a memory of past happiness with a loved one.

In fact all these expressions were partly a response to the beach photographer's professional 'Smile Please,' partly a result of having the noonday sun in their eyes, and as Paul held the bleached and curling rectangle of paper in his hand, twenty years on, it was memories of unhappiness, loneliness and frustration that came seeping back.

The trouble began at Scarborough Station. The family set down their collection of brown cardboard suitcases outside the ticket barrier. Elsie fished a card from her navy-blue leatherette handbag with gilt-framed clasp and read off the address: 'Dunedin Hotel, Northdale Road, No Number'.

Paul had never been to the seaside before except on day trips. Certainly he had never in his life been to a hotel. His considerable knowledge of how to proceed in hotels was gained from books, films, and 'Paul Temple'. He knew just what Paul Temple, or Cary Grant and all those people who commonly lived among hotels, cocktails, white telephones and servants, would have done.

'I'll go and call a cab,' said Paul Kane, to his father, Alfred Kane.

'Tha'll what?' expostulated Alfred. 'Tha' stands there in thy new mid-blue suit, grey cotton shirt and plain red tie, and tha' says tha'll get a soddin' cab! Who dost think I am, Duke o' Soddin' Gloucester?' 'Nay Alf,' quavered Elsie. Alf ignored her. 'Get hold of yon case, lad, I'll give thee cabs, I'll gi' thee bloody cabs!' They asked a porter the way.

They carried their cases along Northway and the poetically named Columbus Ravine, found that Northdale Road crossed Dean Road, chose the right-hand section i.e. chose wrongly, back tracked, and located the Dunedin Hotel after nearly half a sweaty, bad-tempered hour. To Paul's disappointment it looked much more like a rather big house than the glamorous assemblage of bell-boys, lifts, receptionists and restaurants that his imagination had created around the word 'Hotel'.

Mrs Moore showed them their room. Up two flights of stairs covered with a deep-pile brown carpet, patterned with a red and black motif of conventionalized flowers and held in place by shiny brass stair rods.

High Tea would be at six, said Mrs Moore.

'What the 'ell's 'igh tea?' jested Alf, when Mrs Moore was safely out of the room. 'Do we 'ave to eat stood up, or what?' ''Appen it's on t'roof,' cried Richard and they laughed together, father and son. 'Nay,' said Paul incautiously, 'it nobbut means that there's hot stuff to eat, like a dinner, not just bread and jam and stuff.'

'What does tha' know o' bread and jam and stuff, thee that's had good meat all thy days?' thundered Alfred. 'Is't 'olesome food o' a collier's family not bloody good enough, then? Had tha' begun to distance thyssen from us already, and thee not even passed for yon grammar school, yet? Canst tha' not wait to start thy ruthless social progress, sithee, grounded on t'heroic sacrifices o' a working couple that slogged through t'twenties and thirties, on tea and bread and marge, to a plateau o' prosperity modest enough but sufficin' to give thee thy chance to do the eleven plus, thy chance to join them pansy Wolf Cubs – fancy calling a so-called Cub Pack 'St Margarets' – chance to talk posh, go about calling cabs and go to yon grammar school, and smoothly join t'ranks o' t'possessing and oppressin' classes, no doubt with t'assistance of Public School pansy mates at Oxford and Cambridge or somewhere such?'

'Nay, tha's hard on t'lad,' quavered Elsie.

'Hard. Aye, 'appen,' gritted Alfred. 'But t'ole meritocratic rat-race o' grammar schools seems to me right suspect, tekkin workin' class lads sithee,' he pointed the stubby nicotine-stained forefinger of his right hand at the white-faced Paul, 'and turning 'em into toffs and bosses, or worse, into t'cultural parasites o' t'possessin' classes. Think on, it's so-called "composition" our Paul's best at, not sums nor geography. So he'll not even be a banker nor a boss, sithee – 'e'll most likely write plays i' verse or brittle comedies o' manners in t'style o' Noel Coward.'

''Appen Paul'll write plays or novels o' satire and protest?' quavered Elsie, ''Is social rapprochment to middle class ways o' goin' on is very like to come about, seeing e's off to t'grammar school but that doesna' mean 'e's bound to go over to t'side o' t'toffs politically an all.' 'Aye,' said Alf with heavy irony, 'aye 'appen e'll turn out to be a left wing intellectual. That would be all right that would. That'd make us all feel it were worthwhile, t'starvation, t'Depression, t'roof-falls, rats, outside lavatories, Tizer . . .'

'I think our Paul's daft,' chimed in Richard.

There was a long, awkward silence, broken suddenly by a rattling noise at the door of the bedroom. Richard it was who opened the door and in trotted muddied, exhausted and limping, but full of joy, Rex and Prince.

'For Chrissake,' interjected Johnson, 'get rid of those bloody dogs.'

'They've escaped and followed the family as in "Lassie", "Incredible Journey" and other instances, rather a good if unoriginal touch I thought. Also I don't know quite how to end the scene without them,' protested Kipling.

'Look. Point One – how far is it from Mexthorpe to Scarborough? And why Scarborough, not Filey, by the way?'

'I failed to get hold of a street map of Filey whereas a plan of Scarborough is in the back of my road atlas. The distance by rail Scarborough-Mexthorpe would be eighty miles or so changing at York, I suppose – why do you ask?'

'OK, the Kanes make it in, say, four hours by train plus a bit of walking. The dynamic dog-duo make it in four hours plus five minutes i.e. averaging twenty mph. How? Hang-gliding?'

'Good point. I must delay the dogs' arrival.'

'Forget dogs. Really. Some film producer is going to love this script with dogs, he'll give it to some Disney-type director and what have you got? "Rex, the story of a Dawg." How do you fancy people stopping you in the street saying "Wow! are you the Kipling who wrote 'Rex – Story of a Dawg' – I cried, you know at the bit where that kid, what's his name – says 'Being a dawg means never having to say you're sorry.'" What would your mother say? "My son the dog-story writer?" That would make her proud? Point B, you are obviously just using these dogs instead of death. They are Death Dogs. Anytime you're stuck plot-wise, shazzam! there's one or more dogs battering the bloody door down. Hey, how did they get through the front door of Dunedin Hotel, by the way? How did they get past Mrs Moore? They said they'd come to read the meter?'

Kipling reluctantly excised the dogs. 'I think you may be right if as usual a shade immoderate in expression. I am using these creatures as rather transparent plot-devices. But how can I end the scene?'

'They all go downstairs for tea, *natürlich*. Alf finds that High Tea really is hot chips and stuff, he feels a new respect for Paul's worldly *savoir-faire*.'

'Yes. Going down for tea – but no new respect, I think, not yet.'

The week passed. In Paul's memory it remained as a little string of dismaying cameos of his father's contempt. Sometimes tiny scenes, his father in a cafe asking a waitress in a black dress largely covered by a serviceable blue pinafore with one large pocket, for an extra cream-horn for 'my lad Paul, e's off to Grammar School, tha' knows, it'll be all marrons glacés and millefeuilles then, but 'e mun' mek do wi' cream 'orns for now, eh?'

Longer scenes, too. Paul built a square sandcastle measuring some four feet by four, having reasonably well-compacted bucket-shaped towers at each corner, and a fair moat, varying in depth from six to eight inches. Paul, as an imaginative child, was well aware of the conventional style of his castle and had originally planned a more challenging motte and bailey construction. But with his unusual insight and sensitivity to other people's moods, he had deliberately not built a castle that would seem in any way 'queer', 'know-all', or merit any of the other terms of abuse which all his actions seemed to attract from his father and Richard in that humiliating week.

His disappointment was sharp, then, when his father barely glanced at his castle, but merely said, 'Come over 'ere, see what Richard's done, sithee, by 'eck. That's what tha' shoulda' done, summat that showed pride in thy 'eritage, summat that modestly, like, but sincerely exemplifies t'principles o'socialist realism.'

Richard had dug down into the sand, rather than built above it, and had created a fair facsimile, measuring some six feet by eight and penetrating some four feet below the surface, of Mexthorpe Main Colliery.

'I'd a gone deeper,' said Richard. 'But struck water, tha' knows.'

'Aye, 'tis a bugger, sithee, striking water,' agreed Alf. Man to man, as it were. That was the day the beach photographer took the snapshot of the Kane family caught, to all appearances, at a moment of luminous happiness. Later that afternoon Richard and Alf went off together to stone seagulls. Paul stayed with his mother. She knitted, using 3-ply mustard yellow wool, he was listlessly reading Frost's *Complete Poems*.

Paul's relationship with his mother was at an awkward stage. He was too old to sit on her knee or bring her grubby bunches of daisies in a jamjar, yet too young to pick her up by the waist, kiss her and tell her she was his favourite girl. Stranded now between those two safe islands of acceptable mother-son behaviour, they spoke little these days, and the talk was always of life's business – Had he fed the dog? What was there for dinner? How did he come by that grazed knee? Where was his cap, he'd be late for cubs? Paul was surprised, then, when Elsie spoke: 'Paul, tha' must not pay too much 'eed to thy dad's mood, just now. 'E's troubled in 'is mind tha' knows by all this stuff that's int' news just now.'

'You mean General Neguib's seizure o' power in Egypt, mam?' queried Paul.

'Nay, nay,' Elsie shook her head. 'That there European Coal and Steel Community agreement come into force last week. Thy dad sees it as nobbut a cloak for international European capitalism to mek a comeback, tek us all back to t'days of low wages, pit-closures and weak unions, pit nationalization notwithstanding.'

'I understand now, sithee,' replied Paul, 'but why pick on me, mam?' he queried. 'Well,' went on Elsie, 'rightly or no thy dad sees thee as a symbol o' t'future in which Butler Education Act and all them fine principles o' 1945 are peverted sithee, so that nowt fundamental comes to pass, nowt save a few bright whelps like thee bein' skimmed off top of 't'working class to merge into t'same old elitist structures.'

'I see now,' said Paul quietly.

For all his intelligence and imagination it had never struck Paul so forcibly before that his own life could be touched so by far-away events beyond his control, and, at the age of ten, still even beyond his complete comprehension. A chill breeze sprang up from the east.

'Wow, I like that,' said Johnson. 'Great. Just one or two little things. Why does Paul's dad have it in for the wolf cubs? "pansy wolf cubs". I quote. I seem to remember that in the conception scene Alf actually spoke favourably of Baden-Powell. So what's the problem?'

'Actually, I just put that in from my own experience.

When I was a cub, myself, our troop was called '89th Hertfordshire, St Margaret's'. It was sewn onto the sleeve of the uniform, and I remember feeling a bit of a fool with it on. 89th Hertfordshire sounded suitably military, but 'St Margaret's' sounded, well, soppy. I imagined Alf as a coal miner and so on would feel the same about a cub-pack called St Margaret's – just a small personal touch.'

'Maybe there's a bigger thing here. Maybe Alf's against the cub thing because it's church-connected. How about if Alf is a militant atheist and Paul gets religion via the wolf cubs? Also, cubs and brownies etc., are always good for a laugh and you could do with a comic scene or two, its all pretty serious, so far. What if Paul has a grandad, who is nice and also religious, whereas Alf is more sort of grim – he sounds a right bastard actually – and very unreligious and leftwing. Hang on, that might not sound very fair to the left. Got it – grandad is nice and religious but really wet, like that berk in *Hard Times* who won't join the Union and falls down a mineshaft. You could even let grandad fall down a mineshaft, if you like, as a sort of treat for you – provided he only does it once and entirely on his own. He could be a Catholic, or Jewish, that would be good, he could be like that ghastly old oaf who talks to God in "Fiddler on the Roof". So anyway he's godly and a berk and eventually falls down a mineshaft but before that he talks Paul into joining the cubs, leading to much comic business ref cubs. Also what about a big passing-of-the-eleven-plus scene, all rejoicing and things then someone breaks in with news that grandad has fallen down the mineshaft, sort of laughter and tears thing?'

'Who would bring the bad news?' asked Kipling, evidently a little bemused.

'Who cares? Rex and Prince if you like. It's a detail. What do you think of the whole idea?'

'This would all be inserted before the seaside scene? I see. So there's religious conflict, comedy scenes with the cubs, a Catholic or Jewish grandfather and a mineshaft. And the eleven plus. Do you think it might all be rather confusing?'

'Do one thing at a time. Do a cubs comedy thing first, based on another snapshot and work it from there.'

'It will mean renumbering all the pages,' sighed Kipling. 'But I think in principle these ideas are very useful. Thank you.'

A Partial Re-Start

On April 11th 1951 President Truman relieved General McArthur of his command in Korea. On that same day, Paul Kane had his photograph taken in his cub uniform.

The photograph was in black and white but twenty years on Paul could remember every detail of that uniform. Green cap with yellow piping, dark green jersey, royal blue neckerchief, held in a small leather clasp known as a yoddle, grey socks, with bright green tabs attached to the garters. Best of all, were the badges: red blue & white. These were sewn onto the right hand side of the jersey and spoke to the world of Paul's skill in life-saving and woodcraft. Best of the best was the single vertical white stripe, some four inches long down the left side of the jersey, which showed Paul's status as a sixer, a leader of his kind.

The least pleasing part of the uniform was the strip of white tape on the jersey's left arm which bore in red letters, the name of the pack – Third Mexthorpe Saint Margaret's.

Paul had been born into a world of war, and still lived in an age of conscription. Young men 'joined up', got 'called up', appeared in uniform as a matter of course. All Paul's young life he had been aware of soldiers' uniforms and especially of the powerful and romantic legends on the shoulder-flashes of those uniforms. Inspired by the 'Duke of Wellington's Regiment' the 'Royal Artillery', all his conscious life he had looked forward to having his own shoulder-flash on his own uniform. And now he had it. And because the local cub pack was vaguely affiliated to St Margaret's Church the shoulder flash was deeply unsatisfactory. In Richard Kane's brutal term it sounded 'pansy'.

The shoulder-flash was a small thing, though, compared to the glow of pleasure that Paul gained from his uniform and from everything associated with the cubs. This loyalty to the Scout and Cub movement and to the 3rd Mexthorpe St Margaret's in particular was undinted by the ludicrous incidents inseparable from the efforts of a small number of dedicated but sometimes unskilled adults to direct the violent energies of a large number of small boys.

There was the hilarious occasion when the khaki shorts of Mr Greenwood suddenly fell down about his ankles during his explanation of the reef-knot. There was the unforgettable occasion when the white, blue-trimmed knickers of Arkela (otherwise Miss Bennett of Class 1) fell around her ankles as she recited the Cubs' Promise. At the opening of the new Scout and Cub Hut in the summer of 1950, the herringbone tweed trousers of the Regional Commissioner fell about his ankles as he concluded his stirring address. Paul himself and his peers at camp in the Peak District constantly fell into rivers, ponds and streams, and were often chased hilariously by flocks of sheep or herds of bullocks. Their attempts at simple camp cookery, of course, invariably ended in some side-splittingly comical misadventure.

'How did you make up the cub comedy bits?' asked Johnson. 'Out of my head,' replied Kipling.

'It might be perhaps a good idea if you read a bit of, say, Tom Sharpe, just for the odd extra inspiration,' said Johnson tentatively.

This well-meant suggestion led to hours of frustration for Kipling as he tried to devise a comic scenario *au* Sharpe which would involve the total destruction of the

Scout and Cub Hut and adjoining buildings by some form of explosion simultaneous with sexual assault of some kind by Miss Bennett on Mr Greenwood or vice versa, and the eruption of a herd of bullocks or other animals onto the scene, all within a framework of day-to-day plausibility.

In the end it was decided to leave the comic or rather farcical section as it stood; the section was already in Johnson's opinion, very funny and as he said, would gain in comic impact from the relative sombreness of some of the neighbouring passages. It was then agreed that the character of grandad should be introduced without further delay, but here a slight difficulty was encountered.

In Kipling's preliminary sketch of the introductory scene 'grandad' talked with Paul about religion, politics and human relations, as well as inducting him into gentle countryside skills such as bird-watching, angling and rock-climbing and into reading of a quietist but not effete type such as *Little Women* or the works of Charlotte Yonge. Kipling also drew up an outline of a scene to which we have already referred, the scene in which Paul takes leave of his grandfather to go to Oxford leaving the old man hurt and bewildered. As Johnson pointed out, such a literate and well informed grandparent would be more likely to have coached Paul for the Oxford scholarship papers than to be reduced to tears of hurt and incomprehension by the idea of Paul leaving Mexthorpe to follow his natural academic destiny.

Kipling eventually agreed, but was unwilling simply to tear up the farewell scene on which he had spent much time, and so conceived the idea of having two grandparents (a) the maternal grandparent, coarse, ignorant, uncouth but warm hearted, who could figure in the pathetic farewell scene, and (b) the paternal grandfather, the gentle, thoughtful one who would converse with Paul on religion, nature etc.

Johnson thought this solution sexist and an interesting discussion followed on whether the representation of a man as ignorant and uncouth could be seen as an attack on women, merely because the man in question is the father of a woman. Though not wholly convinced by Johnson's case, Kipling, in deference to the evident strength of Johnson's feeling, decided to retain an ignorant and uncouth grandfather for purposes such as the farewell scene, and put the education of Paul in spiritual matters, and the study of nature and the gentler side in the hands of a grandmother.

Johnson found the idea of grandmother showing Paul how to bait fishhooks and cycling up Kinderscout with Paul to look at the sunset and the like, not plausible. Kipling, in turn, found Johnson's objections both sexist and ageist.

Finally in a mood of impatience rather than of true inspiration Kipling decided that the representative of more spiritual attitudes to life than those of Paul's loving but formidable father, should be an uncle and not a grandparent of any sort.

Neither Johnson nor Kipling were at first very pleased with this solution. Johnson, particularly retained for some time an oddly personal hostility to the uncle character. When, for instance, it was decided that the uncle should be an ex-miner debarred by injury from further work in the pit, Johnson suggested a range of disabilities so ghastly and comprehensive that Kipling was forced to point out that a blind paraplegic would find practical difficulties in instructing Paul in bird-watching and rock-climbing and that to hold such a view did not mean that one was prejudiced against the handicapped. Similarly, when the two were working out together a reasonably light job for the uncle to take up after leaving the pit, Kipling rejected, coolly and very firmly, Johnson's unhelpful suggestions of pimp and male prostitute.

In the end Johnson's attitude softened, but it is an interesting reflection that it was in this unpromising manner that there was conceived one of the book's most movingly and vividly portrayed characters, a character who is indeed already regarded by a few critics as one of the major creations of twentieth-century English Literature – Uncle Ted.

Kipling skilfully wove the first appearance of Uncle Ted into Paul's memories of days in the wolf cubs:

> Uncle Ted was at the house the day that Paul asked to join the cubs. 'Can I join t'Wolf Cubs, dad?' he piped. 'Ay, tha can an' welcome lad,' replied his father. 'Yon Baden-Powell's t'only one o' t'so-called aristocracy ever did owt for t'working class. Tha'll learn discipline and solidarity in t'ranks o' t'Cubs lad, also survival skills to do wi' knots and life under canvas.'
>
> Uncle Ted was drinking tea from a pint mug. He was wearing brown corduroy trousers, an unbuttoned navy blue waistcoat and a blue collarless shirt that fine June evening in 1949. 'I think,' he said mildly, 'tha's a shade strong in thy judgements on t'aristocracy Alfred. What about t'noble Lord Shaftesbury and his strenuous campaign in respect o' Child Labour?'
>
> 'Lord Bloody Shaftesbury!' expostulated Alfred. 'Nobbut served t'interest of t'landowning party agin t'millowners sithee, by gum!' 'Well, I'd personally, like, put Christian charity somewhere into an account o' Shaftesbury's motivations,' murmured Uncle Ted, 'But we'll not quarrel over things long gone, rather follow t'spirit of reconciliation represented by t'recent moves by t'western Allies to include Germany in t'European Recovery Programme. Join t'Cubs lad,' this to Paul. 'Remember, learn what tha' can, where tha' can, when tha' can, from whomsoever tha' can, in whatsoever way tha' can by whatever means tha' can, by sunlight or moonlight, candlelight or lamplight, summer or winter, fair weather or foul. Make that thy motto, and tha'll not go far wrong. Even if its nobbut knot-tying or firelighting, tha' never knows when it might come to pass that there's a knot to be

tied for our Lord or a fire to be lit for all mankind.'

There were many questions young Paul would have liked to ask at that moment but Uncle Ted went on: 'Ay, a sheepshank for Jesus, sticks rubbed together, to save a soul. Who knows, who can know, 'ow can it be known? It'll be St Margaret's troop tha'll be joinin'?'

'Ay,' said Paul, eagerly, 'They 'ave blue neckerchiefs and are organized in five patrols, namely Owls, Foxes, Eagles . . .'

'Saint Bloody Margaret's?' growled Alf and drank noisily from his pint pot of tea. 'What sort o'bloody name is that for a gang o' colliers' lads? Best join Girl Guides if tha' wants to be a St Margaret's holy Joe!'

'Thy underpants are St Michaels tha' knows Alf,' put in Elsie, waspishly.

'Yon's altogether different,' glowered Alf. 'Think on, our Paul, I've publicly said you can join and join tha' shall but I'll not 'ave thee made a pansy, nor yet a bloody parson.' He glanced fiercely at Uncle Ted, his great fist white-knuckled around his pint pot and Paul could sense undercurrents and ripples of feeling that went far beyond the question of his joining the Wolf Cubs.

'Nay, let's not fall out over a name,' said Uncle Ted mildly. 'St Margaret's it is, by chance though it could as well 'ave been St Paul's or St John's or St Mark's, sithee or St Matthew's or All Saints or some purely and entirely secular title, such as 89th Mexthorpe or 4th South Yorks or 30th West Yorks, they'd all be appropriate, dwelling as we do in Mexthorpe and in t'West Riding and in t'area traditionally known as South Yorkshire. The numbers of course I picked at random as illustrations or examples. T'main thing is, let not our divergences o' view and emphasis o'ershadow t'lads desire to associate himself with a movement we both approve like, from our legitimately differing perspectives.'

'Tha's allus 'ad a silver tongue, Ted,' grunted Alf.

71

The incident was closed. Paul's young mind slipped away from the rest of the conversation towards green caps and red badges, Owls and Eagles. But at the same time, the wisp of an idea remained that Uncle Ted represented something. Something different from dad, something he could not even give a name to yet. Something important.

Johnson suggested as an amendment to this scene that Alf should kill Uncle Ted with a blow of his great fist and/or pint pot but Kipling good humouredly put this unconstructive suggestion (which would obviously have led to appalling plot-complications, the disposal of Uncle Ted's body being merely one of the first and most obvious) down to Johnson's irrational dislike of the Uncle Ted character as such.

'Seriously, though, I still think it should be a grand-father,' said Johnson grudgingly. 'But leaving that aside you know, it's really coming on, you know. Really. I think you can forget the apprenticeship bit. This is the end of the beginning. That scene you had, you know, thingy. I think you're possibly now at the real start of things, writing-wise. Really.'

'Well, perhaps a journeyman, let's say,' said Kipling cautiously.

Journeyman Days. The Real Beginning

Kipling pursued vigorously the theme of Paul's relationship with Uncle Ted.

Uncle Ted had been a collier in his day until a roof-fall in 1930, a few days short of his twentieth birthday, injured his back. 1930 was not a good time for even a slightly disabled ex-miner to be looking for work and Ted spent six black years unemployed. Slowly though, he learned a little of the plumber's trade, did a few days house-painting here and there and finally was able to get himself taken on as a general labourer and handyman in a small firm of builders. Now, after the war, he was secure enough but the irregularity of work in the building trade meant that he often had an odd morning or afternoon to spare for his favourite nephew, Paul.

He showed Paul how to fish for tench and roach and chub and trout in the canal. Often they did not fish at all though. The rods, the brown thermos flask, the old light-green tea-caddy containing the spam sandwiches would be stacked by the bicycles and Paul and Uncle Ted would just look at the life of the canal. To a casual eye, the canal was a strip of brown water, running between banks of purple-blue bricks, varied by nothing more interesting than the odd iridescent skim of oil. But Uncle Ted's eye was not a casual one and his soft voice would quietly guide Paul's eyes to a hundred things he would never have seen unaided. Things like the caddis flies and their larvae, the water-beetles, water-boatmen and skimmers, the dragon-fly, the frogs and toads and the newts splendid in their orange spotted skins. Things like the kingcups and sedges, marsh-marigolds and bull-rushes, the water rats and voles, the rare prize of the glimpse of an otter and her cubs at play. Birds to Paul were rather uninteresting little brown creatures until Ted quietly pointed out the sedge warbler and willow-warbler, the moorhen, the kingfisher and the regal heron.

'All these have their part to play, sithee,' murmured Uncle Ted, the day they saw the heron. 'Mr Heron eats big fish, big fish eat smaller fish or fry as they are often known or take dragonfly larvae, and dragon-fly larvae take damsel-fly, damsel-fly take tiny creatures too small for us to see, and so it goes. It's a hard way for some, sithee, but it's t'Lord's way of makin' certain that there's herons about.'

'Why does t'Lord want herons?' queried Paul innocently.

'Why lad, so they'll be there for me and thee to learn about, and improve ourselves by t'learning and

73

knowing more and more o'such things. There's more ways to learn than out of books, tha' knows, there's learnin' by observation, by experience, by deduction, from combined experience and observation, by deduction from some a priori position . . .' 'Aye,' broke in Paul, excitedly, 'and by induction from a given set o' circumstances like.'

'That's t'way, young Paul,' Uncle Ted smiled quietly. 'But keep thy voice down lest tha' fright Mr Heron.'

'That's a nice little scene,' was Johnson's comment, 'but why could Paul not see a heron?' Kipling was somewhat at a loss.

'It says here,' continued Johnson, that 'Ted blah, blah, would guide Paul's eyes to a hundred things he would never have seen unaided.' How could you miss seeing a heron, they're about eight feet high aren't they? How about making clear that "Paul's sight was already damaged by much close reading so he could not even see a heron unless . . ."'

'No, no, it's simple carelessness on my part. I'd better put something like, "things Paul would never have seen etc., and also things he would have seen but would not have understood the full meaning of. . ." Yes, that's better . . . I think I also might take out one or two of those creatures anyway, it struck me as I was writing that the fauna was too rich for a canal in a mining district but biology is certainly not my field and I wanted to give an effect of kaleidoscopic, abundant life you understand. Was there anything else?'

'Well, just one thing – where's brother Richard?'

'Oh Lord, yes. He would want to come along I suppose. I'll just say that he went off with his gang of big boys.'

'What if you ran a sort of counterpoint thing with Richard? Richard tags along on the canal trips but is beastly – chucks stones at the newts and herons, scoffs all the sandwiches et al? Wait a bit – that's no good.

Never even see any sodding herons etc., with him crashing about chucking rocks, obviously. How about this instead? Richard goes off with his gang doing things that would please Dad, i.e. butch, positive, left-wing, contrasting powerfully with Paul and Uncle Ted's gentle bourgeois pursuits. What if, say Richard plus gang went up to the middle-class area, throwing bricks at cats and rabbits etc., as an act of class revenge while Paul and Uncle Ted are peacefully watching the newts and voles and things? And later you could have Uncle Ted explaining quietly about, e.g. the water cycle and rain etc., while Richard's gang are peeing in the reservoir as a vandalistic act of class revenge.'

'But all social classes drink the water in the common supply,' Kipling objected.

'Yes, but Richard and his maladjusted mates are too thick to know that. They think only the toffs get lovely clear reservoir water, everybody else gets it out of sewers or something. Anyway, each day the two kids come back to Alma Terrace, and report to Dad on what they have been up to and the bad kid Richard gets OK'd and the good kid, i.e. Paul, gets slagged off for being a wimp a bit like in *King Lear*, like a fairy tale. A mythic element. Myths are big just now you know.'

'How would all this affect Paul? Do we really want him to grow up strongly influenced by Uncle Ted or merely treat Ted as a pleasant and instructive companion but not ultimately a model?'

'Say he gets to be just like Uncle Ted, until he's at Oxford. Then he goes to join the University Liberal Club and says something like:

"Hello! I'm Paul, a Yorkshire miner's son but I've not turned out to be a boring Commie berk as you would expect because of my Uncle Ted. By teaching me about newts and the water-cycle etc., he has shown me that God likes moderation and everything so here I am, ready to become a Liberal, like Jesus no doubt was." Then these Liberal-type posh undergraduates cry, "I say, Henry, throw this awful bounder into the street," and they do and while he's lying there in the street he realizes that Uncle Ted was OK on herons etc., but his analysis of the class war lacked rigour. Wow: we could even start the book there! Like this: "As Paul Kane lay on his face on the wet pavement outside the Oxford University Liberal Club he wondered. 'How did I get here? Who am I? Was Uncle Ted wrong all along?' On April 7th 1941 very similar thoughts had passed through the heads of General Archibald Wavell and Adolf Hitler" . . . get the idea?'

'It's very ambitious. I'll have to think about it. I think just for the moment I'll carry on with the Uncle Ted theme and get away from biology onto safer ground.' So it was provisionally agreed.

There were many sides to Uncle Ted's wisdom. One day he and Paul were at the canal edge, quietly fishing, when Ted suddenly asked, 'Does't thou see owt special, different or out o' t'ordinary, Paul, about top two courses of brick in yonder canal bank lining?' Paul looked across the brown water to the opposite bank. 'Yes,' he squeaked excitedly, 'they're a paler blue than t'other courses, also each brick is longer, by up to an eighth of an inch than them in t'lower courses. Why is it so?'

'This way, sithee. This cut, or canal, were originally dug in t'year of our Lord 1799. One Sir Montague Smith had it dug – to mek employment for t'local poor and to carry coal from his pits to t'poor folk o' Goole who had no pits o' their own then. It were therefore called Mexthorpe–Goole Canal i' them days. Now then, by t'year 1814, canal wasna' doin' so well for trade, for numerous and various reasons some simple, some more complicated and t'canal bank brickwork, also certain locks, toll-houses and so forth were falling into decay. So sooner than see t'canal fall into ruin and t'poor folk of Goole deprived o' coal Sir Montague sold all to a Christian family called Fairbrother. They took it off his hands and joined all t'canals i' South Yorkshire into what they called t'Yorkshire Union Junction Canal, that is to say precisely the very name it bears today.' Paul's eyes were shining with eager interest, 'But what about them bricks?' 'That's exactly what I asked mysel'' continued Uncle Ted. 'Was it, I asked, inwardly, was it just that local fashions i' brickwork changed from time o' t'initial work of 1799 to when t'repairs were carried out in 1814–15 by Fairbrothers? Or was there summat more, summat deeper goin' on by gow?' He paused, smiling at Paul's eager impatience. 'Any road, what I found out, were this. Sir Montague got his bricks, t'original bricks o' 1799, sithee, those of darker shade, from t'Laisterside Brickworks at Batley set up in 1790 by Josiah Adams. But . . .' he paused, with the skill of a true storyteller, 'But, comes 1814, Josiah Adams had passed away and t'Brickworks had shut! What they were to do, Fairbrothers, I mean? Where were they to seek bricks now? Well, after long search they found a suitable brickyard, that of Grice of Wakefield, established 1805. And they, that's to say Grice's brickyard, provided bricks for t'work, only of a slightly different cast from t'ould bricks as tha' can see to this day.' Paul was round-eyed ''Ow does tha' know all this, uncle?' 'By consulting parish, municipal, and other records and also contemporary newspapers i' t'Record Office, and tracing this story step by step. I'll tek thee when tha's older if th' likes,' he added, seemingly casually. 'Oh yes, to t'Record Office, yes please, uncle!' exclaimed Paul, his imagination alight. 'History' to Paul, had hitherto meant only dull school history tales of Christopher Columbus, Alexander the Great and the like. Now, in a few minutes, he had learned to see that it could be a thing exciting and vivid, something quite literally springing from his own physical environment. 'When tha's older. That's a promise, a deal. I give thee my word,' said Uncle Ted with his quiet smile.

'Well,' was Johnson's comment. 'I've got to say I'm starting to like it. I see the nature bit shot in slow motion, with vaseline on the lens and something nice from Mozart, dream-like quality, close-ups of dragonflies, newts etc. We could even have the history of the canal bit told by Uncle Ted in voiceover and actual shots of zillions of 18th-century-type navvies digging it – more sort of Aaron Copland music then, I think. Sir Matthew could be a nice cameo for Olivier, his face betraying only a scintilla of emotion as he signs away the canal. Then the famous end bit from Beethoven's Ninth as the new light blue bricks are finally stuck on.'

'Well, I'm glad you approve – where do you think we should move from here?'

'Shelve Ted. Only for a bit, I mean. We want a bit of action, I'd say, some more visual emphasis and some more links with 20th-century history.

'This was roughly the time of the Bevanite split in the Labour Party in 1951. Perhaps Paul could have a fight with Richard over the issues involved?'

'Nice one. Only it would involve sketching out quite a subtle political position for dumbo Richard, either Bevanite or pro-Attlee, we could hardly make either of them Tory, endless complications, that.'

'I tend to agree. What about the Festival of Britain?'

'Not very contentious though, was it? Hey though, what about that big thing they had stuck up – Skylon? What if that induced phallic fantasies in Paul, thus cueing a doctors' and nurses' bit with what's her name or somebody?'

'I think the historical tie-in would appear contrived, frankly. Perhaps I can work out the thing more subtly.'

'OK. But hang on to the visual, remember,' said Johnson.

Kipling then set to work on the most ambitious piece of plot construction and character manipulation he had so far attempted.

'23 April 1951 was a big day for Mr Brian Marks.

Mr Marks was nineteen and a trainee teacher. He was dressing that morning, before going out to face his very first class. His very first class was Class 3, Paul Kane's class, at Mexthorpe Junior Mixed.

What to wear was a problem. Mr Marks wanted to impress the teachers at Mexthorpe Junior Mixed as sober, mature, with just the faintest, most tactful hint of a marginal social superiority. So no garish ties. On the other hand, he was afraid of giving to the working-class rough diamonds of Class 3 Mexthorpe JM the slightest reason to feel nervous of him as 'posh', so, no cuff-links, no separate stiff collar. He had chosen thus, to wear an eggshell blue, collar-attached shirt, characterless navy blue tie, dark brown sports coat, dark grey flannels, dark tan shoes, well polished.

None of this forethought availed him, however, at 9.11 a.m. on 23 April when he found himself alone with Class 3. The sin he had committed in the eyes of Class 3 was inexpiable and had nothing to do with dress. He was a man. Men were not teachers, except extremely old men who were headmasters. Other men who taught in junior schools must be cissies and treated accordingly.

Brian Owen, wearing a soiled grey jumper, dark grey trousers and steel-framed spectacles with a cracked left lens, began the 'treatment' at 9.11 plus thirty seconds by banging his heavy, unpolished black boots rhythmically on the wooden floor.

'Who's doing that?' enquired Mr Marks. 'Brian Owen, Miss,' smirked Roger Knowles in a genuine but unfortunately phrased attempt to curry favour. Coarse laughter erupted. 'Stand up, Brian Owen,' boomed Mr Marks. Freda Mitchell wearing her usual emerald green cardigan over a gym-slip, with short white socks and tan sandals, stood up. 'Sit down,' bellowed Mr Marks. Half the class stood up. 'Sit down or I shall be obliged to call upon the headmaster to administer corporal punishment either to all of you or to an arbitrarily selected group,' gritted Mr Marks.

This threat worked for the moment. Mr Marks began to talk about the Central Plain of Scotland. Brian Owen and others began to plan further actions against the cissy. Paul Kane's plan was subtler than that of most of his fellows. It involved questioning Mr Marks at some appropriate moment about the latest state of research on the date of the Roman evacuation of Scotland's famous Antonine Wall. Paul felt instinctively sure that Mr Marks' knowledge was imperfect in that contentious area and also Paul would be quite safe from any threat of reprisal since he would have committed no identifiable sin.

Brian Owen flicked a large pellet compounded of chewed foolscap paper and black school ink, which fell near Mr Marks' well polished shoes. No reprisal followed.

At intervals similar pellets were flicked by Gavin Bailey, a fair-haired boy wearing a brown corduroy lumberjacket, Wilfred Jackson, a red-haired boy dressed in a single breasted brown jacket over a navy blue jumper and grey trousers, Barbara Gee, an unusually tall girl with black hair in two plaits, wearing a lemon yellow cardigan, and Lance West, a diminutive boy in a bright red jumper and very scuffed dark brown shoes.

Mr Marks ground on through the Scottish Central Plain, for twenty-five very long minutes. At 9.36 Paul's chance came. 'Any questions?' asked Mr Marks. Paul's hand, signalling the poisoned chalice of his question on the Antonine Wall was half way up, when he paused. 'Think on,' he thought, 'e's nobbut young, this Marks bloke. And considerin' the circumstances, his treatment o' t'Central Plain wasna' that bad, though I don't think 'e stressed t'nodal importance o' Stirling enough, nor yet t'geological background. On t'other hand 'is pedagogic technique were right poor – 'e could 'ave provided 'isself wi' a proper map, or at least wi' chalks of more than one colour.' The hand began to move up. 'And yet, by gum, 'appen all these preparations wi' chalk and maps were done indeed – but our disorderly conduct's driven all from t'poor chap's mind so it's us to blame, not 'im . . Though think on, sithee, young or not, 'e's still *in loco parentis* and we're *in statu pupillari*.' As Paul considered, his kindliness and sensitivity at war with his desire to see justice done and professional standards upheld, the moment passed. Mr Marks went back to his exposition of the Central Plain, the steady rain of pellets continued until it was replaced by a hail of small nodules of green or grey plasticine and, towards ten o'clock, by a shower of darts made from thick brown or grey paper. As playtime approached, this in turn was replaced by a mixed volley of the contents of the pencil cases of those children, mostly girls, who owned such cases, a volley comprising pencils, crayons, rubbers, pencil sharpeners, small wooden rulers and pairs of brass compasses. As a parting gesture of contempt just before rushing out as the playtime bell clanged, the children hurled the wooden pencil boxes themselves which were mostly some six to eight inches by three inches and often decorated with floral pattern transfers.

Paul, as the top of the class sat farthest from the door and so was the last to leave. 'You,' cried Mr Marks as Paul approached the light-blue painted door. Paul turned 'I've got my eye on you, boy, don't think I haven't.' 'But I've done nowt!' Paul ejaculated. 'I've taken no part in the hurling of improvised missiles and other forms of irregular behaviour that's characterized t'last hour or so!'

'I had noticed that. I'm not a fool, you know, and I know just what you're up to. Now get out!'

Sensing that this was not the moment for further discussion, Paul went out.

'What do you think so far?' asked Kipling, 'the historical references will be coming in later, by the way.'

'Fine. Are the kids going to have another lesson with Marks after playtime?'

'Oh yes, necessarily. Marks for instance has not yet explained what he thinks Paul is 'up to' as it were. It's just left in the air. I plan for it to be a Maths lesson, if you are afraid it could be too monotonous.'

'No, it's just the kids have nothing left to chuck at him.'

'Drat. You're right. Just my careless planning again, I'm afraid. Perhaps Marks could make them pick up the mess before the next lesson . . .'

'And then they fling it back at him. Great. Sort of ironic. Or how about if they spend playtime gathering new missiles e.g. lumps of coal. Then they bombard the putative pouf with pieces of coal as hewn by their butch dads, symbolically. Great visual scene.'

'Well I will obviously have to think through the details of the next lesson again. Coal is certainly a possibility, or clods of earth perhaps.'

'What does Marks think Paul is "up to" by the way?'

'Well, truth to tell, I haven't thought that out yet. Actually the incident is based on something that happened to me as a boy. There was a classroom riot at my prep. school with a new teacher in Geography and I took absolutely no part in it . . .'

'Well, what was your game then? What were you up to?'

'Nothing. I was just interested in the lesson. But when I told them that, I was beaten for insolence.'

'I suppose we could reproduce that, though it's a bit far-fetched for a basically naturalistic book. Or we could have Marks come clean on his theory ref. Paul. But what the hell could his theory be, granted he is not actually unhinged by his experience?'

'I don't know,' said Kipling gloomily.

'Why not just say that they never saw Mr Marks again?'

'You mean arrange for his sudden death? I thought you were very opposed to that sort of thing?'

82

'No, no, the authorities just zonk him back to college. After all the classroom's now thigh deep in missiles. People would probably notice.'

'I think on the whole that would be best, given the logistic and psychological problems we are meeting.'

And so it was decided.

Class 3 never saw Mr Marks again. An unmarked blue van took him back to college. After playtime Miss Galloway took them for arithmetic.

Alfred was off work with a twisted knee that day and Uncle Ted had suffered a recurrence of his old back trouble, and so was also not working, deciding instead to have a stroll round to 12 Alma Terrace for a pot of tea. So it came about that when Paul reached home Alf and Ted were both there.

'Na' then Paul,' smiled Uncle Ted, 'what sort o' day's it been at school?' Paul told them of Mr Marks' unhappy debut as a teacher.

'Tha' did reet Paul to say nowt about that Antonine Wall,' said his father. 'Poor sod were punished enough by t'sound o'nt. I'd rather go down t'pit any day than get on t'wrong side o' forty o' yon little buggers and then try and teach 'em summat.'

'Well,' ventured Uncle Ted, 'I'm not entirely sure that I totally agree there. I think it might be said that 'appen t'evil-doer, or even t'mere incompetent should 'ave his due and right meed meted out from t'point o' view o' God's justice, also of profitable chastisement, profitable to t'chastised one, I mean, sithee, so that he'll learn, and mend his ways. Mr Marks' strange response to you at t'end o' t'lesson 'appen shows that he had not learned enough humility, like from the events o' t'lesson this morning.'

'Aye,' cried Paul eagerly, 'that thought crossed my mind an' all – was I 'appen depriving Mr Marks o' a positively creative experience even though at t'time it might seem to 'im like nobbut a further humiliation.'

'Compassion,' went on Uncle Ted, 'shouldna' be

confused wi' sentimentality – I only offer that as a talking point, o' course, tha'll understand.'

'Bloody 'ell,' expostulated Alf. 'Tha' means to say, Ted, it's good for a chap's soul, and pleasin' to God an' all, to 'ave a load o'pellets and other objects chucked at 'im and then 'ave 'is ignorance o' t'Antonine Wall showed up straight after.' He crashed his great fist on the table, causing the pint mugs and the big brown teapot to rattle on the green check-patterned oil-cloth.

'Suffering can be spiritually creative and redemptive,' smiled Uncle Ted, 'and even i' thy secular philosophy, Alf, there might be room, sithee, for t'notion o' humiliation being cathartic or therapeutic – only wi' due moderation of course.'

'Soddin' 'ell,' cried Alf, the great veins standing out on his forehead, his face flushed. 'If tha' favours sufferin' so much that means tha' stands, no doubt, wi' them as would cut t'National 'Ealth for t'sake o' weapons o' mass destruction, tha' stands wi' Attlee agin Nye Bevan and 'Arold Wilson! That's where thy Christianity leaves thee!'

'Well', said Uncle Ted mildly. 'I do think, possibly, Mr Bevan and Mr Wilson could be seen as misguided to oppose t'will o' their lawful superior, Mr Attlee that is to say. And t'defence o' t'nation agin evil-doers . . .'

'Comes afore compassion to babes and sucklin's, afore pity for t'sick and 'elpless, afore all t'natural promptin's o' t'gentle and compassionate side o' man's nature!' So saying Alf crashed down both his ham-like fists on the table causing the mugs, teapot, tea-caddy and many other light objects in the room to rattle furiously. His face was scarlet, his lips drawn back in a wolf-like grin of pure rage, his trunk and arms trembled with the effort of self-control.

'I can see I've touched on a sensitive issue, sithee,' said Uncle Ted, 'and moreover I'm sure Mr Bevan and Mr Wilson, bein' experienced men of affairs and i't' case of Mr Wilson, a graduate, acted in their view for t'best, and who's to say that time and tide and t'passage o' years and long avenues o' History will not show that they acted pleasingly in t'sight o' t'Lord, 'appen?'

'Tha's got t'gift o' bloody words Ted. 'Ave another pot o' tea,' growled Alf, mollified. 'And what's thy view, young Paul?'

Paul thought long before replying.

'Am right interested 'ow a metaphysical creed based ont' principle o' divine love can finish up tekkin' a more punitive view o' a given case than an avowedly secular, materialistic socialism, sithee, but I don't rightly know who's in t'right. Another thing, it's interestin' 'ow such a parochial thing as t'conduct of me towards Mr Marks so closely reflects big things, like t'world o' grown-up politics. Can I go out to play 'til teatime now dad?'

'Get the idea?' asked Kipling, tentatively. 'Does the irony work?' 'Wow, yes and the running together of Paul's mini-world and the real Bevan type stuff is great. One small thing – isn't it odd that Uncle Ted, with an allegedly bad back, goes for a stroll round to Alma Terrace?'

'I could not think of another way of getting the two men together in the house before Paul arrives at approximately 4.05 p.m. on a working day. I agree it does not read very plausibly.'

'Could he be carried round from wherever he lives, on a stretcher? Then you could have more characters in it, a sort of Brueghelesque mob of onlookers. You needn't write lines for them, the people who carried him, I mean, they could just gasp and things if necessary. Or form a silent, sinister backdrop. Also, think how effective, irony-wise, Ted on an actual NHS stretcher, in pain, running down the NHS and saying "Kick Bevan, Buy Bombs etc . . ." don't you think?'

'Why would he be so keen to talk to Alf that he would actually have himself carried to 12 Alma Terrace with a painful back?'

'To discuss the Nye Bevan thing, *natürlich*. This Uncle Ted is a deeply earnest, concerned bloke, he'd want to talk about it straight off. Also think! They could be discussing it as Paul comes in. At the moment, they are not apparently saying anything to each other as Paul comes in, which would surely not be in character for those two.'

'Good point. But who would carry Uncle Ted round? Two people or four? And why aren't they themselves at work?' asked Kipling.

'Four miners. On their way to the evening shift, their white teeth grinning in their coal-blackened, good-natured faces etc. Then they could be long gone before Paul arrives if you prefer, requiring no lines, no clothes, no nothing.'

'Thank you, very good, I'll work on that. But their faces would not be black on their way towards the mine, surely?'

'I don't think so. Though actually they're *always* black on '50s type newsreels aren't they? Make them be on the way home, then, to be on the safe side.'

On this, as on countless other occasions Kipling provided the basic shape and emotional rationale of an episode and Johnson's patient help in chipping away at the details of sequence and credibility allowed Kipling to transform the competent to the exceptional. Few readers of the novel will forget this scene in its final version, as the slight, pain-racked figure of Uncle Ted on his stretcher quietly argues the retributive case against Mr Marks and the general case for submission to lawful authority, to suffering and to prescription charges; while Alf, towering massively over him, makes his ferocious case for compassion, love and free medical care.

A New Dimension (1)

'I have been wondering,' said Kipling, 'how to manage

the matter of Paul's passing of the eleven-plus. It's obviously a highlight of his young life but on the other hand, not at all dramatic in itself. His success, after all, could hardly have been a great surprise to anybody.'

'Yes, tricky. How did they actually let them know, by the way?'

'My notes indicate that the commonest method before 1955 was for the local authority to send a letter to the school, who then gave it to the child, who then, well, took it home.'

'Yes. Not really gripping, story-line wise, is it? Hey, what if something awful happens to the letter? Suppose Paul gets home all chuffed, gripping the vital foolscap envelope and Prince maliciously grabs it out of his hand?'

'Possible. Then perhaps Rex, sensing in some way the importance of the letter to Paul, fights Prince for it? No, I think not. After all, the local authority could just send another letter, it would merely be drama for the sake of drama.'

'You're right. Here – why concentrate solely on Paul? Let him take his letter home, nice quick scene, then follow some of the other kids in the class home with their letters. That way you can sketch in some of the other people in the village – give a bit of epic-type depth etc. A new dimension.'

'What a good idea! Perhaps we could also as it were briefly follow up one or two who did not get a letter?'

'Good thinking.'

It was in this next episode that the novel indeed began to take on a new dimension of complexity, a feeling of being a portrait of a community and a time, as well as the story of an individual which it had, frankly, somewhat lacked up to that point.

March 1953 saw the visit of Marshal Tito to London and also the arrival of the eleven-plus results at Mexthorpe Junior School. At three o'clock the Headmaster, Mr Royd, came into Paul's classroom, wearing a dark-brown two-piece suit with a lighter brown pin stripe, white shirt and light blue tie. Everybody knew why he had come. His broad smile and the small clutch of long white envelopes in his hand would have told the least aware of children that these were the letters for those who had 'passed for the Grammar School'.

'You all know what these are,' announced Mr Royd and began to read the names on the envelopes without more elaboration. 'Gavin Bailey.' Paul felt a little jolt of dread. He was quietly confident of passing, but was fractionally disconcerted not to be the first name read out. Was it in some sort of order? 'Peter Bannister'. Alphabetical order. Relief. 'Paul Kane'. Total relief. Four more names: Roger Knowles, John Martin, Freda Mitchell, Brian Owen. The seven chosen children were each given a long white envelope and told to 'run home with it, give it to your mam and come straight back'.

Elsie was doing the washing when Paul got home.

'It's me grammar school letter!' cried Paul. 'Or at least so it seems to be widely assumed, like!' She wiped the suds from her right hand on her plain blue pinafore. 'Gi's it 'ere then.' She read the name and address slowly. 'It's addressed to thy dad. Let's leave it ont' mantelpiece for 'im to open at shift end. He'll be that proud.' 'Ay,' agreed Paul. 'That's both technically correct, seein' it's addressed to dad, and also sensitive and thoughtful, tha' knows, sithee.'

'Ay. And so am I proud. Right proud,' choked Elsie, 'off tha' goes now.'

As the door closed behind Paul, Elsie sank to her knees, the held-back tears flowing freely now.

'Oh Lord,' she prayed, 'tha' knows I'm not a religious woman. Not an atheist tha'll understand, more like indifferent, normally. But I thank thee now that thou hast preserved my child, first from the Nazi war-machine that thou sawest fit to destroy utterly afore it could do him ill. Then hast thou preserved him through t'measles and other childish ills, trivial i' themselves but capable o' turning nasty through complications. And now thou hast opened t'gates o' knowledge truth and goodness to my child Paul through this thy crownin' mercy to date.'

Paul kicked stones as he ran back to school whistling. He scored five goals for Sheffield Wednesday, all brilliant solo efforts.

At that point Johnson raised an objection.

'Don't you think Elsie's prayer is a bit hard on old Richard? I mean he goes to the Sec. Mod. presumably, right? So is he excluded thereby from goodness truth and things? In her view, I mean?'

'Fair point. We certainly don't want her to seem indifferent or hostile to Richard. Perhaps she could after the prayer give Richard's dog, Prince, a bone or something of the sort to show that she loves Richard equally well? I don't really want to write some wearisome scene where she actually explains to Richard that she loves him even though he failed the eleven-plus.'

'Sorry, that's not on. "Hullo luv, Paul's going to the Grammar School unlike you, you thick pratt. But I gave Prince half a pound of Bonio, so that's OK isn't it?" Not a very clear logical connection is it? No, I think the reference to Richard should be in the actual prayer.'

'Something like,' suggested Kipling, 'Oh, Lord, er, I mean by all this no disrespect to the other forms of opportunity which thou hast opened to Richard by, er, allowing him to fail for the grammar school or wait a moment, allowing him to pass for the secondary modern, according to his less academic but equally valuable bent.'

'Yes fine, something like that exactly. Great.'

And so it was agreed, and Kipling moved on to the main business of the episode, the brilliant, impressionistic depiction of the Mexthorpe community, through the spreading news of the eleven-plus results.

Roger Knowles went in through the brown-painted

back door of 'Knowles – General Grocer', the shop on the corner of Alma Terrace and Inkerman Street. His father was in the back room, carefully adding small quantities of fine white sand to half-pound bags of sugar. 'What's up?' he snapped, the pale brown eyes in his ratlike face curiously matching his brown overall.

'It's me grammar school pass,' smirked Roger.

His father said nothing but carefully opened the white envelope, putting it on one side for re-use. His lip twitched as he read the letter. 'Good lad,' he said finally, 'now we'll show these riff-raff round here. Show them what's what. Take a shilling from the till, lad, you've done me proud.'

Roger opened the till, rang up 'no sale' and quietly palmed a two-shilling piece. 'Thanks dad,' he leered.

'Who else passed?' asked Mr Knowles.

'Paul Kane, Freda Mitchell . . .'

'Mitchell!' expostulated Knowles senior. 'That dratted pauper's brat. I'll stop her mam's credit. That'll show 'er.'

Roger sniggered his approval.

The object of their malice, Freda Mitchell, red-haired, pale-skinned and wearing, as ever, her emerald green cardigan with a grey skirt and brown lace-up shoes, reached home at that moment. 'Home' was a tiny house in Sebastopol Street. 'Mam,' she said simply, 'I've passed for t'grammar school, ere's t'letter.' Her mother as pale skinned and red-haired as Freda, glanced up dully from the old brown overcoat she was tearing into strips to make into a rug. She read the letter wearily and sighed.

'Where are we to get brass for school uniform, satchels, and sticks for playin' 'ockey and other such?'

'I'll 'elp thee, mam,' quavered Freda. 'I'll help thee make rugs. I'll cut t'overcoats and thee can make up t'rugs.'

'Rugs!' murmured Mrs Mitchell. 'Every 'ouse in Mexthorpe 'as one of our rugs by now. Some 'as two.

They think I don't realize. They buy 'em out o' pity since thy dad went missin' i' Normandy. But that's nigh on ten years since, and folks 'll get fed up o' rugs made out o' overcoats, fed up o' pity, fed up o' charity, fed up of us. Then that'll be t'finish.' She coughed harshly. 'They'll chuck us out o' this house. I'm nine weeks behind wi' t'rent now. Then we'll be on t'street. They'll tek thee into a Home or orphanage o' some sort. And I'll do mysel' in, 'appen.'

The piles of worn out overcoats on the floor and on the chairs, the strips of discarded sacking for the rug-backs, seemed to mock them.

'But I'll not spoil thy big day, lass,' Mrs Mitchell smiled palely. 'Look in t'drawer and get yon green jellybaby out. I've been savin' it for such a day. Think on, don't chew it all up at once.'

Brian Owen's reception was different. Two of his elder brothers, Charlie and Bob and his big sisters, Carol and Rose, were at home, playing truant from the secondary modern school. Brian was glad for the thousandth time that his eldest brother Edwin was in Borstal and that his sister Lorna had run away from home, for those two had always taken savage delight in tormenting Brian the 'clever little bugger, teacher's pet'.

As it was Charlie slapped him sharply across the mouth, and Carol snatched away his battered spectacles and gave them to the two-year old Harry to play with.

'Gi' us that soddin' letter,' gritted Bob and snatched it from Brian's grubby hand. 'What's tha' doin' wi' letters, tha' little pillock? It's about bloody grammar school, I'll bet.' Bob could not read, but had plenty of animal cunning. He began to tear the envelope up, slowly.

'Gi' it 'ere, yer little bugger,' boomed Mrs Owen, and cuffing Bob aside with her great forearm she snatched the letter. Her fifteen-stone frame strained at her grubby dark blue dress with white floral pattern, white revers and cuffs.

'It's about t'grammar school,' quavered Brian. 'Eh?' queried Mrs Owen her wide red face creased by a look of cow-like puzzlement. 'I'll best give it to t'maister.'

'Wake up yer bastard,' she bellowed and kicked Brian's portly, balding father who was asleep in a ruinous blue armchair, wearing bleached overalls and a collarless grey shirt. 'What's up, yer soddin' cow?' queried Mr Owen blearily. 'It's a letter, it's about grammar school, you drunken bugger.'

Mr Owen peered briefly at the letter, blew his nose on it, threw it on the back of the dankly smouldering fire and went back to sleep. For a moment there was no sound in the room except that of the toddler Harry beating Brian's spectacles rhythmically on the damply peeling wall. Charlie laughed.

John Martin, Peter Bannister and Gavin Bailey had receptions which varied in quality and outcome according to the social status and domestic mores of their respective families, and so the seven letters were delivered. But while seven children had letters to take home thirty-two of Paul's class had no letter that day, which meant they were not destined for the grammar school. One such was Wilf Jackson, a lively boy with dark red hair, who on that day was wearing a brown corduroy lumber-jacket.

''Allo mam,' he cried cheerfully as he reached his home a little after four o'clock. His voice was as cheery as ever but something in his manner must have betrayed him.

'You've failed, 'aven't you?' snapped his mother, a pretty blonde woman in a dark green wrapover pinafore. 'Nay mam, 'ave not been selected for t'grammar school reet enough, but I've been selected for a different type of secondary education more suited . . .' 'Failed!' his mother sobbed. 'Tha's ruined thy life and ours an all. 'Ow can we face folks? Tha'll 'ave to go down t'pit, like thy dad, tha'll die i'poverty and ignorance like a beast as tha'll live i'darkness an' squalor, like a beast.'

'I think you get another chance, like, at thirteen,' quavered Wilf. 'There'll be no more chances, no more!' she shrieked. 'Tha's doomed, finished, canst tha' not grasp it, tha' poor little wretch, cans't tha' not understand. Nay, tha' can understand nowt, nowt. That's why tha's failed!' she laughed hysterically.

She was still sobbing when Wilf's father got home, weary and grimed from the pit. He sat on a newspaper in the best chair, an armchair of orange-brown uncut moquette, as she told him, as best she could between sobs.

'Calm thysel', lass. Cryin' and tekkin on will serve no turn. It's end o' all dreams and death of all hopes. T'only way forrard for t'lad now is down, right enough. But try not to sadden t'lad, 'e's done 'is best, didn't tha' Wilf? totally useless and pathetically ineffective though that best turned out to be.'

There was a brief silence.

''Ere lad, don't be downcast, there's still things to live for, tha' knows, though Christ knows what. 'Ere's tuppence, go an buy a *Beano* to read, 'ave yourself a bit of a laugh.'

So the news good and bad, ill and well received, spread through the little town that spring evening, as the mist gathered, and Marshal Tito formerly J. Broz, agitator and Soviet agent, turned his thoughts towards the state dinner with the Queen of England some four hours ahead.

'I like the range, the sweep very much,' said Johnson. 'I like Lorna Owen, especially.'

'Who?' Kipling asked.

'Lorna Owen, sister of Brian Owen the kid with big, fun family – she's run away from home, not to join Moral Rearmament know what I mean? She must be about sixteen–seventeen with sadistic tendencies. Wow! What a part for some Bardot *de nos jours*. Say she meets

Paul . . .'

'No,' said Kipling firmly.

'Say she meets Tito?' persisted Johnson.

'If you insist on re-introducing her, then I insist she meets Rex and Prince who push her down a mineshaft,' said Kipling grimly. 'There is in any case another more important matter I would like your opinion on. Paul is now ready to go to the grammar school. I thought this might be a good moment for yet another new dimension as it were, that is, a rather more experimental type of prose. Also, I would like to drop having to describe these dratted snapshots.'

'Good idea. Go ahead. Do it now when you've got the urge,' said Johnson, eagerly supportive.

A New Dimension (2)

The grammar school day began with blessings and signs. Metal blessings, zinc watering cans, steel shears, serrated things. A window to breathe on and draw swastikas in your breath on Holdsworth's window. Mr Holdsworth, worthy to behold, bald, counting flypapers, nodding in blessing. Then at your service, Yorkshire Traction. Wheels bigger than you think. Yes sir, fifty years we've been at it man and boy, no sir, not yet sir we have quite frankly not moved her yet, but spare us another half-century of your time, sir and we will move her sir, we will tract her so speak. Yorkshire, with splitting of gears and smell of burnt rubber if necessary will be tracted, there will be light to be seen between Yorkshire and adjacent counties bless you, sir no doubt of it.

Legends within. Lower Saloon 26. Upper Saloon, 30. Lower your head when leaving your seat. PRESS ONCE.

Lower your head when leaving your seat. Walk like lions not like horses. Like lions, then, alight with care. The final blessing and sign 171. Lamp standard of no special colour but 171 is white, like the word of God and dims scrupulously little every day – every seven years it is renewed, in the night, a white revival. If it were renewed more frequently, there might be fewer damned.

'"Lamp standard no special colour" could be tricky,' said Johnson, 'perhaps we'll shoot this bit in black and white, sort of dreamlike.'

'But it's not too obscure?' asked Kipling. 'It may be experimental but I want it to be clear. Could you as it were translate it?'

'Well, they start the day at the Grammar School with like assembly, *natürlich* – blessings etc. And there's this Holdsworth, who's a sort of lay preacher and an ironmonger. Also a Nazi – hence swastikas. Then Paul dreams or day-dreams about somebody trying to shift Yorkshire, symbolizing his own desire to get away to Oxford or somewhere. Then there's this lamp standard number 171 which is symbolic.'

'Would it help if I made clear that Yorkshire Traction is the name of the local bus company?' asked Kipling.

'Bingo – yes – he gets on a bus and sort of fantasises about dragging Yorkshire about using buses.'

'What about "Lower your head when leaving your seat"?'

'Well, when Paul gets off the bus he, er, lowers his head. But like a lion, not like a horse.'

'Why not like a horse?' Kipling was relentless.

'Horses symbolize pit-ponies i.e. all he hates and fears etc. So does the metal stuff, watering cans etc. They symbolize Sheffield and everything so he draws swastikas on the window to sort of distance himself. From Sheffield.'

'And what do you make of "Press Once"?'

'Perhaps he is remembering wistfully his young love Betty thing, that he only got to press once before they broke up over "The Mummy's Curse", could it be?'

'Your tone is interrogative, rather than explanatory.'

'Sod it, they don't have to get every word, it's not the

Yellow Pages, its supposed to be demanding if its experimental. In bits anyway. Some of them might think Tito was a Jap, but so what? Footnotes we're not going to give them.'

Kipling thought it would be a good idea to have some tea.

'Have you thought?' asked Johnson after a while, 'of experimenting with content rather than form? It's all the thing. The language is quite ordinary but what actually happens is like weird. Why not have a quick look at some Borges and Marquez?'

Kipling read Borges and Marquez assiduously but not with great profit. His first and only draft of an attempt to adapt the technique of those Latin American masters to his own purposes read as follows:

Paul swung up onto the bus, his first day brown grammar school cap was a sun of dark light. The conductor gave him a mildewed green ticket, refused to take his money and asked him instead a question, 'Have you a brother?'

'Yes I have a brother, one of his names is Richard.' Paul cleared himself a space to sit, among pigeons and moribund rabbits. 'I too had a brother. He was murdered. I was a colonel in my own country, when I avenged my brother it was necessary to leave. I became a bus conductor here. I am happy.' After an hour or two hours, the bus moved off. The pigeons settled to dream.

'What happens next?' asked Johnson.

'Paul is very late for school,' replied Kipling a little coolly. 'He explains to his form-master that the world of the Yorkshire Traction Company is one in which conventional time values do not obtain, and that his lateness must be seen as a mythic rather than an objective event. He produces the mildewed corpse of a rabbit in evidence. The form master produces a bone-handled knife, cuts a joint from the rabbit, eats it ravenously and I don't really think it's going to work.'

'Could you sort of play it down? Suppose Paul is in like an ordinary geometry lesson and he thinks his set-square is a mildewed rabbit, just briefly?'

'I think that if that sort of thing happened in a generally naturalistic setting Paul, as an intelligent child, could be expected to seek psychiatric help.'

'What about Kafka then? He's doing this sum, say, Paul, I mean, and its quite easy like two into twenty three or something only it goes on and on and he can't finish it and he uses up all the exercise books in the school, and he still symbolically can't finish it so he turns into a beetle. For a bit. Then he turns back, of course.'

'I think, on reflection,' said Kipling, 'that slavish following of any model, either Central European or Latin American, is not appropriate. I must find my own distinctive voice, my own gloss as it were, on that naturalistic tradition in which I am after all most comfortable. I think actually, I may have an idea on how to do it. I've roughed this out if you care to have a look.'

The Kanes could not afford the whole school uniform, but the official letter had said that grammar school cap and tie would be enough. So Paul set out, in his good grey herringbone patterned tweed coat, and grey short trousers, crowned as it were by the brown grammar school cap with its matching red-striped grammar school tie. It would have been good to have the brown blazer as well, especially for the sake of the huge, heraldic Grammar School badge covering the whole breast pocket. But, as Paul reflected, as he swung off the bus platform a second before the vehicle stopped and walked confidently through the wrought iron school gates, his outfit. imperfect as it might be, was in no way comparable with a two-piece suit made out of green curtain material with a red floral pattern.

His confidence was not dented either by his lack of a proper satchel. As he looked round the crowded playground he saw leather satchels of various shapes and sizes and a good sprinkling of new looking briefcases, but no one else on that whole densely populated asphalt plain had a cheap green canvas satchel like his. He observed the fact with mild interest but no trace of embarrassment.

It was five to nine on 12 September 1953. Nikita Khrushchev was about to be appointed First Secretary of the Central Committee of the Soviet Communist Party and Paul Kane was about to become a Grammar School Boy.

He went up to a large, surly-looking dark-haired youth of about sixteen.

'I'm a new lad,' he said, 'where do we 'ave to go, sithee?'

'Ah!' the surly face broke into a broad smile. 'Malleson's the name. Shake! Are you a scholarship-kid? Jolly good. Well, in that case I expect you'll be in 3B. Go through that big door there when the bell goes, then second door along the corridor on the left. Good luck!'

A little later, Paul and some two dozen other eleven-year-old boys were standing, fiddling with satchels and scraping their feet, outside a blue painted door marked '3B'.

Paul's preparation for the moment, mostly through carefully reading dozens of school stories and also through two attentive viewings of the film of *Tom Brown's Schooldays*, had been thorough. He knew exactly what to do next.

'What's thy name?' he asked a small pale-faced boy wearing owlish National Health glasses. 'John Green,' said the boy smiling hopefully. Paul hit John Green not very hard in the stomach, causing tears to spring to Green's eyes, more from shock than pain.

'Right, I'm Paul Kane, think on, and I'm going to be t'class bully. I'll be t'school bully afore I'm done an' all. Any objections?'

There were bigger boys and stronger boys in the rough circle that had formed around Paul and Green but Paul had chosen his time with great psychological insight so that no one, in that moment of general uncertainty and apprehensiveness, cared to challenge him. At about 8.59 on 12 September 1953, Paul became the bully of Class 3B.

Mr Dickinson arrived, small, rotund, in neat, threepiece black suit which made him look like a large seal. He was wearing an MA gown, which enchanted Paul who had never seen such a creature as a gowned schoolmaster in the flesh. This was something like!

They shambled in noisily, sat down in individual swing-top desks. Mr Dickinson called the register: 'Butterfield, Green, Kane'. He glanced up. 'Who's Kane? Not going to live up to your name I hope?' His tone was only mock severe as Paul instantly perceived.

'Nay I 'ope so an' all, sir', smiled Paul. 'Have to knock some of the edge off that accent, though,' murmured Mr Dickinson coldly. There were sniggers. 'Leeson, Mann, Neil . .' 'Sir, I 'ope that gainin' cheap sniggers at t'expense o' my accent's not going to be a part o' thy pedagogic policy,' cried Paul. 'I'd regard that sort o' tactic as not up to snuff, sithee for a place o' t'status o' this school, no more than weak puns on a lad's name. More address and sensitivity than that's professionally required o' thee, sir surely?' Mr Dickinson blushed, 'I'm sorry, I only meant, er, I must finish the register. Parker, Phillips . . .'

The bell rang for assembly. As they filed out of the classroom, Paul quietly but firmly kicked John Green's ankle.

Johnson said nothing for a long time. 'What's that bit about a suit made of green flower-patterned curtain material?' he asked finally.

Kipling explained. 'I saw a film about 1949 or 1950 about a working-class child, an orphan. I think he was Irish. Anyway he went to a new school somewhere and lacked proper clothes. So his grandmother made him a suit out of green curtain material with red flowers. She was either totally unimaginative, or indifferent to the effect his appearance would have on his new school-mates. Naturally he was instantly humiliated and beaten up, first by the boys, then in their different fashion by the teachers. I can't remember the film's name. He became a doctor, eventually. But even at medical school he kept catching pneumonia because of the great holes in his shoe-soles. Anyway, the matter of the green curtain-suit seems to me to sum up the tedious conventionality of the way in which writers treat First Day as a theme at New School – listen to this rough summary I made of the literature – First Day at New School (boys) beaten up (11 cases) humiliated by teachers (14 cases) sneered at by boys/teachers for dress, physical appearance, accent, religion, etc. (15 cases) run home in tears (4 cases) afraid to go to school at all (2 cases) run away from new school and killed by passing tram (1 case). And so it goes. So the idea is that this glancing reference to green flowered suits is a hermetic clue to the total overturning of convention which awaits the reader in the rest of the passage.'

'It's a great idea,' said Johnson. 'Just one thing. If you carry it through he ought to fail 'O' level, get expelled for nasty crimes, etc. So how does he get to Oxford? Ultimate academic success is as much of a cliché as getting duffed up on day one. Also, if he's going to go round clogging everybody, might he not lose sympathy, readerwise, I mean?'

'Yes, those are difficulties. Also, now I come to think of it there is the matter of sport, which I had not considered. Incompetence at sport and sporting prowess are both clichés in accounts of school life in roughly equal measure.'

'Well, that's easy, he could be great at cricket and lousy at football. Hey, how about this. He's a split personality. Monday to Wednesday he's a nasty bully and thick with it, then every Wednesday at dinner time he becomes sensitive and brainy and everything for the rest of the week?'

'How could we account for such bizarre behaviour?'

'Brain damage: something falls on his head. No, that's crude. What if he's torn between the butch life-stance of his dad and the wimpish ideas of Uncle Ted? Unable to decide this fundamental clash of values etc., he consciously decides to split the week fairly between them.'

'Or,' said Kipling eagerly. 'It could be much more refined if he were to display certain behaviours in certain subjects. He could be intelligent and so on in English, also in say History and French the other 'A' levels he will need, and in Latin and Maths for the University entrance requirements. In other non-essential areas, say Geography and German he could be the sort of anti-social yob and failure who normally only figures in this sort of literature very peripherally. Seriously – what happens one wonders, to the cheats and bullies of schooldays? People certainly do not write their biographies it seems.'

'Right. You don't see: "The young Aldred from his first days at Tonbridge showed himself to be a congenital liar and pathological bully, qualities which were to stand him in good stead when in time he entered the wider world of publishing and the arts" – never see that, do you? No chance. What about sex though?'

'What about it?' asked Kipling cautiously.

'Well, when he's like fourteen is he going to be coarsely successful behind the bike sheds and crudely taunt other kids etc., or more gentle and sensitive and shy and things. Or sort of torn? Sort of torn could make some good scenes. Tender and shy etc. with Jill Boggins until say, midnight – no, they wouldn't stop out that late in those days – until say 10.15, then from 10.15, all crude and lewd and horrible.'

'We must be careful not to make the boy sound like Count Dracula. I think on reflection it would be best if after all I made it clear that Paul does the bullying and so on as a conscious front, a protection merely for a sensitive and intelligent persona. This would take us away from the area of abnormal psychology we seem to be drifting towards. I'll have a look at the episode again.'

Kipling provisionally re-drafted the end of the first day episode as follows:

> The bell rang for assembly. As they filed out, Paul quietly spoke to John Green. 'Nowt personal, Green. It's just I 'ave to establish myself as t'bully or 'appen be bullied in my turn sithee. You just 'appened to be t'nearest small lad for me to cuff. If tha' likes, after I've made thy life a misery for three or four years tha' can fight me in t'yard and I'll knock 'ell out o' thee publicly but tha'll gain folks' respect and also self-respect sithee for t'game way tha' stands up to me all covered in blood but spiritually unbowed.' Green smiled gratefully. 'Thanks, Kane.'
>
> The corridor leading to the hall was a long one, and Paul had time also for a quick word with Mr Dickinson.
>
> 'I 'ope you'll not think, sir, as how I'm normally cheeky and also drearily lacking t'ability to take a joke. Only I must seize t'fleeting opportunity o' this first day to make sure that if anybody's goin' to be t'butt o' thy jokes and sarcasm and so forth it'll not be me.'
>
> 'Quite understood,' smiled Mr Dickinson. 'And very sensible. Could you perhaps suggest anyone else for the role of class butt?' 'Green might 'appen be suitable, sir,' ventured Paul.

A Problem and an Adjustment of Direction

'Good, great,' said Johnson. 'Where do we go from here?'

'I thought I would explore the growing cultural gulf between Paul and his family, especially his father. I thought to do it through a series of vignettes based on short lessons, for instance an English lesson could be used to show up the growing linguistic gulf in accent and usage, an algebra lesson could show Paul developing habits of logical thought, contrasting with his parents warm-hearted left-wing but muddled thinking – and so on.'

'Well yes, but there's one thing, its just a management thing really, but what about Bailey, Bannister, and evil Knowles, Martin, Mitchell and Brian Owen?'

'Oh God! They went to the Grammar School as well, you're absolutely right. Also Wilf Jackson and all the others who failed, they would still be around in the street in some sort of relationship to Paul I suppose. Or were grammar school entrants sent to Coventry, as it were, by their peers who failed to get in? Do you think I should start a card-index of these characters? And what am I to say about these wretched brats anyway?'

'Steady on, no need for panic,' soothed Johnson. 'Point one – all the eleven-plus failures can just sink out of sight. Nobody will notice. You can't see the *Times Lit.* saying "This is a masterpiece but flawed seriously by the failure to tell us more about Wilf Jackson", can you? Right. Point two – the other kids who passed for the GS. What if they were all Catholic and went to some RC place?'

'Contrived,' said Kipling.

'Agreed. What if you just do a thumbnail sketch on each one? e.g. Bailey went on to get 'O' levels in Maths, Chemistry, Art and German, got in the cricket 2nd XI and left school to become an undertaker's runner or something, and he and Paul lost touch?'

'But who would care to read such an uninteresting recital?'

'OK. This is better. At first Paul was friendly with the other Mexthorpe kids but very soon he was drawn into the glamorous orbit of Jeremy and Sebastian, i.e. little middle-class pseuds – then you could develop these new middle-class kids a bit, and give them some plot to be in.'

'Why not develop Bailey or some other of the Mexthorpe Boys?'

'Because Jeremy and Sebastian talk English and you can drop the by gum, sithee stuff. Also they can have cars and take Paul up the Dales and things and lend him books and stuff. And they would have TV. If he hurries up and chums up with them pronto he can still catch "The Quatermass Experiment". Oh, God, another thing – what about grandad? If you want a big farewell scene with Paul and grandad in circa 1960, shouldn't we have the old thing sort of introduced by now?'

'Yes, certainly. You know, I think I must start a card-index of characters, actually. Also I think you are right about Paul's friends. His induction into the middle-class should start now, though in a mild way, so that Oxford can still present him with cultural shocks of various kinds. But the most urgent thing is, as you say, to introduce grandad without more ado, so the family is all assembled before the next phase.'

This was agreed, and Kipling set to work.

'Go round and see thy grandad, Paul,' said Elsie at the end of that first shiny week of grammar school life. 'Tek 'im some o' thy new school books to see. 'E can't read, but 'e knows what books are. It'll please him. 'Ave a nice talk wi' t'old lad. Just don't bring up t'recent electoral victory of t'Christian Democrats i' Germany. Tha' knows 'ow 'e goes off t'deep end at stuff like that.'

Paul never knocked at grandad's door. Grandad would have been offended if blood relations did not use his home as their own but stood knocking 'like t'bloody insurance man or summat'.

'It's me, grandad. I've some books to show thee from t'new school I go to now to illustrate t'new intellectual world I inhabit now, sithee.'

'By 'ell,' chortled grandad. 'Set 'em ere on t'table.' He indicated a table some five feet by three covered in a yellow and white checked cotton table-cloth. Paul produced C.V. Durrell's bright red algebra book.

'This 'ere is algebra, grandad. It's a mathematical system, sithee, in which numbers are replaced by letters so allowing much greater flexibility in certain

104

kinds o' calculations.' Grandad fingered the shiny red book gingerly.

'Nay, what's world comin' to!' he cried, 'there were no algebra down Mexthorpe Main i' 1908 when t'flood swept away sixteen colliers and t'bosses sealed shaft so t'corpses are down there yet, all to save a few bloody quid.'

'I think algebra was known in 1908, grandad, but 'appen it wasn't applied, like, to mining engineerin' problems wi' sufficient skill,' said Paul in a conciliatory tone.

'Ay. What's this blue book, then?' queried grandad vaguely.

'That,' replied Paul, 'is French. It's called *En Route*, meaning 'on the way', signifying sithee that the reader is on the way to a mastery of French language and culture.' 'Nay, nay, that my little lad's little lad should be speakin' i' tongues!' ejaculated grandad. 'Tha's lost to us, lost to us! Ay, lost as if thee lay i' t'grave.' Tears filled his watery old blue eyes. 'Tha'll reck no more o' t'pit nor pitmen nor faggots nor picky stick nor snap tins wi' pictures o' t'owd Queen on 'em, nor nowt o' t'distinctive plebeian culture that's bred thee. Algebra! French!' he bowed his old head and wept silently. Paul made an excuse and left.

'When it says "his old watery blue eyes", are they watery normally, or because they are at this moment in time filled with tears?' was Johnson's preliminary query.

'Good point. I will re-phrase to, let us say, "his old blue eyes, watery at the best of times, were now filled with tears".'

'OK. More general sort of point, if he's given up Paul for dead, on account of Algebra and French, now, i.e. in 1953, they're not going to have much to talk about between then and 1960 are they? The big 1960 farewell is a bit pre-empted, isn't it?'

'Perhaps I could bring the farewell forward. This, 1953, is itself the moment of farewell? Then I need not write about the old fool any more at all.'

'But how will Paul explain this to Alf and Elsie? "Run round to grandad's with these faggots and bollocks, our Paul", "Sorry mam, grandad regards me as in some sense dead because of my study of French and Algebra." "Oh all right love, we'll send Richard. Or Rex." Dodgy? eh?'

'Your point is fully taken. I must obviously re-write the passage, or the central dialogue at least.'

This was agreed, and Kipling re-drafted immediately:

> Paul produced Durrell's bright red algebra book.
>
> 'What's yon, then?' queried grandad eagerly, his watery old blue eyes striving to focus the book.
>
> 'It's algebra, grandad. It's a mathematical system, sithee, in which numbers are replaced by letters so allowing greater flexibility in certain kinds o' calculations.'
>
> 'Tha'll not let doin' thy sums wi' letters change thee, like, in thyself?' the old man quavered.
>
> 'It's bound to change my perception o' mathematics, but, sithee, important personality change'll not be necessarily entailed by that, grandad,' said Paul comfortingly.
>
> 'Ay. Good. 'Appen so,' but there was still a flicker of doubt in the old man's watery blue eyes and Paul, therefore, thought it best to make much of the *Dragon Book of English Verse* and the Physics and Geometry text-books and leave the elementary Latin and French primers undisturbed in his green canvas satchel.

Johnson was pleased with the revised version, as well he might be. The subtlety, the fine portrayal of shifting moods in the new version were Kipling's and Kipling's alone, but it was Johnson's sturdy commonsense which had suggested the need for revision in the first place. This is an excellent example of their method of co-operation in action.

The next stage of Paul's story, his first-hand induction into the world of middle-class culture and values through being drawn into a new circle of friends, was obviously artistically and emotionally central to the novel, and Kipling and Johnson agreed, therefore, that it should be opened by a scene of some weight. The first draft read as follows:

At 10.35 on the morning of 15 May 1954, as the French garrison of Dien Bien Phu continued their grim march into North Vietnamese captivity, Paul Kane was munching a mint imperial in the Grammar School yard.

His attention was caught suddenly by a small disturbance. A gang of some half-dozen 3A boys were loudly baiting one of their classmates, a stockily built fair-haired, grey-eyed boy. Paul strode across to the gang. 'Bugger off,' he gritted.

'It's Paul Kane, the 3B bully,' quavered one of the group and he and the rest rapidly scuttled away.

'Thanks!' grinned the fair-haired boy, 'Stephen Brook's the name.' They shook hands. 'I can look after myself you know, but six onto one's a bit much, don't you think?'

'Ay, it is an' all. What were it all about?' queried Paul. 'Oh, politics,' replied Brook airily. 'All I said was that in my view the forthcoming Royal Commonwealth tour was not in any meaningful sense an important event, and they went mad. Anyone would have thought I'd uttered jolly old high treason!'

'I'm surprised though,' said Paul, 'to learn that tha' said as much. I'd have thought thee a person of right-wing orthodox royalist persuasion, looking at thy complete school uniform, obviously new white cotton shirt and tan shoes, and thy shiny new satchel.'

'Oh, I'm a fee-payer, all right,' grinned Stephen Brook. 'But my father, although a barrister, is of markedly left-wing views, specializing in civil liberties and industrial cases. My mother is distantly related to Mr Attlee. She paints, by the way, and my sisters,

Ailsa and Caroline as well as being accomplished musicians, are prominent members of the Communist League of Youth. I've not decided whether I myself will join the CLY until I see how affairs in the USSR develop post-Stalin. You must come up and see us in our spacious house on the edge of town . . . if you want to, that is . . .'

'By gum,' expostulated Paul, 'that would be grand, sithee. I too am not what I appear. Despite bein' a child o' poverty, I've developed wide if unordered cultural interests, through my Uncle Ted, largely. Also, I'm not really a bully, sithee, but rather o' t'pacifist persuasion. We should get along well.'

'Gosh!' said Stephen, 'how pleased my people will be that I've met an actual proletarian!'

'And mine,' replied Paul, 'that I've met a member o' t'intellectual left-wing activist bourgeoisie! By 'eck, it'd be grand if we turned out to be i't same class next year!'

A friendship was born. As the bell signalled playtime's end, all unknown to Paul, it was signalling impending childhood's end, as well.

'I like the bell,' said Johnson. 'Very good, but I think the whole thing gives away rather a lot – these civil liberties and mothers and sisters and things could be sort of leaked out slowly and Paul and Steve could find out about each other more sort of gradually – how about if in this scene, all Stephen finds out is that Paul is not really a rotten bully and Paul finds out Stephen's a bit left-wing, sort of thing?'

'I think that could be a good idea, artistically speaking. Perhaps, also I'd better make Stephen a lot less sturdy, if he is to start off actually afraid of Paul?'

'Good thinking. Oh, and remember to dispose of the mint imperial.'

Kipling set to work again:

. . . savagely crunching the last of the mint imperial, Paul strode across to the group. 'Bugger off,' he gritted hoarsely. 'It's Kane! the 3B bully,' shrieked the boys as they scattered in panic. Only the victim, a slim dark-haired boy, with luminous brown eyes damp with tears, remained, evidently paralysed with fear. He flung his slender long-fingered hand up protectively in front of his face. 'Don't hit me, Kane,' he moaned, and fell to the ground, clutching Paul's knees.

'Nay, get up,' said Paul with gruff gentleness, and lifted the boy to his feet. 'What was t'trouble about, sithee?' he queried. 'Nothing, nothing at all,' whimpered the dark-haired boy, his delicate skin suffused by a blush, his liquid brown eyes unable to meet Paul's.

'Nay, sithee, it must 'ave concerned summat. Logically tha' could not 'ave a row about literally nowt. Also I distinctly 'eard t'phrase "Commonwealth tour" as I strode grimly across t'yard.'

'You know words like "logically" and "literally"?' quavered the dark-eyed boy in wonderment, glancing up at Paul through long black eyelashes.

'Ay, I'm not merely a bully, tha' knows. My cultural horizons might surprise you by their breadth, thanks to my Uncle Ted. But what was t'uproar about?' persisted Paul.

'Well,' stammered the boy, 'I merely opined that the Royal Commonwealth tour was not an event of first rate political importance.'

'Oh!' it was Paul's turn to be surprised. 'Tha's not as posh and right-wing in thy views as thy well-cut uniform, new shoes and crisp new white shirt would suggest, sithee?'

'Not altogether,' said the dark-haired boy quietly, his eyes cast down. 'My name is Stephen Brook,' he went on shyly. 'Perhaps we could meet again sometime and talk.' He touched Paul's sleeve lightly.

'Ay, I'd like that,' said Paul suddenly equally shy.

The bell went. It signalled the end of playtime – and the small beginning of a new direction in Paul's life.

'Well,' said Johnson. 'Great, it's just that it sounds a bit, er . . .' For once Johnson was actually at a loss for words, it seemed.

'Well?'

'Well. Could I suggest a small addition? Could we have Stephen say in the bit where he's terrified, Don't hit me, please, and I'll introduce you to my sisters!

'I suppose so – if you think it would help.'

'Definitely. Also then could Stephen say, let's meet again, I'll bring my sisters, wow you'll like them, and we'll make up a foursome.'

'Actually by "meet again" I intend Stephen to mean something like "meet at playtime tomorrow and share some mint imperials", not a full-blown social occasion. Also I'd imagined the sisters as aged about sixteen to eighteen. That would make an awkward social foursome with two twelve-year olds, surely?'

'Not just for sharing a bag of mint imperials, I'm sure I read somewhere that in Northern Boys' Grammar Schools kids often had their sisters drop by to share the odd gumdrop at playtime, in the fifties especially. It was a sort of tradition.'

'Really?' Kipling was intrigued. 'Do you recall the reference?'

'Not off hand. Anyway, Ailsa, say, could be riding her pony along by the grammar school one playtime and they all share their gumdrops. Maybe Ailsa could actually provide them and they could be After-Eights.'

'Not in 1954, I fear,' interjected Kipling.

'Maltesers, then. Anyway, she's like sixteen and a communist, but sort of haughty and hopelessly out of Paul's reach, *natürlich*, but he's crazy about her. That's why he hangs about Stephen – that's the only reason he bothers with Stephen at all, to be near Ailsa now and then.'

'I'd rather imagined the friendship of Paul and Stephen as sincere and deep.'

'I think you'll have less bother if you write it the way I suggest. Also, let's say Stephen also isn't really that interested in Paul, he's really just interested in, say, Rex and Prince. He's crazy about dogs, you see, and can't have one because his mummy's allergic to fur.'

'It all sounds very tortuous. Why will I have "less bother" as you put it?' asked Kipling, a shade suspiciously. 'Why can't the boys just be very close friends and the sister or sisters and indeed dogs, merely peripheral figures, as in my original vision?'

'Obvious. If you think about it. If Paul remains faithful to the remote but lovely Ailsa until he goes to University, you need not involve him with anyone else. No gropes in the Gaumont, no steamy stocking-tops in the back row at the Ritz.'

'That would certainly save a great deal of trouble – But what of Stephen's motivation? Don't you think that people, readers I mean, will think Stephen very odd to be cultivating Paul merely to have the occasional sight of his dogs?'

'Not at all. I think it will strike a big chord in an awful lot of people. Really.'

Kipling agreed to Johnson's proposed new reading of the situation, not unwillingly, though still a little puzzled, I felt. It was then decided that it would be an excellent idea to turn briefly, for a contrast with the relatively ethereal and subtle matters of Paul's emotional development, to a glance at the grimmer world of his sibling, Richard. Kipling wrote the following brief sketch of Richard's doings on that same spring day which saw Paul meet Stephen Brook:

> Richard's morning had also been eventful.
>
> At fifteen years of age Richard was not far away from the end of his secondary schooling, an experience, which, on the whole he had enjoyed. He had enjoyed the gang-fights, the vandalism, the early initiation into sex behind the rusting school bike-sheds. He had enjoyed helping to drive young Mr

Baxter the Maths teacher into a nervous breakdown. He had enjoyed the organized games, though football and cricket, he thought, would have been better on grass than on a potholed asphalt playground. He had enjoyed the time that old Mr Hardy had dropped and smashed the two test-tubes which constituted the school's entire stock of scientific equipment, he had enjoyed many good days, many a 'good laff'.

But there was a shadow in his mind, a doubt. He wondered why he, and his whole class, were still doing simple adding and take away sums at fifteen, why he still had difficulty reading the *Beano*, why so many of his friends could not even read the *Beano* at all.

That clever little tick, brother Paul, had put his finger on it, one day a few months back. 'In what sense, Richard,' he had asked, 'woulds't tha' say that t'education tha's presently getting is either "Secondary" or "Modern"?'

'Tha' mun well ask,' he had gruffly replied. The penetrating question had lodged in his mind, rankling like an unhealed wound. Gradually the idea had formed that Raglan Road Secondary Modern School had somehow let him down.

The feeling was reinforced that sunny morning by Mr Howells. By everything about Mr Howells. Mr Howells was young, and good-looking in a fleshy sort of way. But every salient feature of him, from his false *bonhomie* to his eyes, too pale a blue and too close together, from his habit of biting his thumbnail to his effortful but not quite accurate attempt to match his brown suit to his brown tie and brown shoes, everything about Mr Howells proclaimed him to be what he was: a non-graduate teacher.

Mr Howells was stumbling through an incoherent account of World War I.

'Right. Then the Americans attacked. Did I tell you they were in the war by this time? Shut up! Well there was this ship, the, er, *Titanic*, and the Germans sunk it in 1917 that was, so the USA came in. Write that down. Sit still, Bates! Anyway the Germans thought they'd better use poison gas, so they got these Zeppelins, who knows how to spell Zeppelin? Stop fiddling, Bates . . .'

Something inside Richard had very suddenly had enough of Mr Howells and enough of much more besides. He took out his pocket-knife and began to carve fiercely at the desk lid, inscribing letters half an inch deep.

'Then there was the Russian Revolution – stop that carving, Kane. Anyway that was in, er, about 1916 . . . write that down.'

Richard ignored him, the chips of yellow wood flew as he carved grimly on.

'Then they got these tanks and Zeppelins, Kane, I told you to stop defacing that desk.' Richard glowered as Mr Howells strode towards him and leaned over the desk to read what Richard had carved in the inkstained wood. 'THE TRIPARTITE SYSTEM IS A BLOODY SWINDELL.'

'I see!' sneered Mr Howells. 'Fancy ourselves, do we? Rather be at the Grammar School, would we? And we can't even spell right can we? First thing we'll do is write out a hundred times "S-W-I-N-D-E-L Swindel has only one 'L' in it". Then we'll fill that carving in with plasticine.'

'Bollocks,' said Richard, suddenly bored with the whole affair.

'Right Kane, *two* hundred times. Now, where were we, oh yes, they got these tanks and Zeppelins and attacked, er, the Germans. Write that down. You as well Bates, you stupid oaf!'

Johnson thought the little scene very effective, but wondered whether most readers would remember what the 'Tripartite system' was. A tentatively suggested solution was for Richard to carve 'THE TRIPARTITE SYSTEM, I.E. A SYSTEM OF SELECTIVE GRAMMAR AND

TECHNICAL SCHOOLS, PLUS NON-SELECTIVE SO-CALLED SECONDARY MODERN SCHOOLS ALLEGEDLY ENJOYING "PARITY OF ESTEEM" IS A BLODY SWINDELL!' He would however obviously have needed a good deal of time to complete such an inscription and as Kipling insisted, Richard's was an act of sudden rage, not of smouldering alienation over a long period.

Johnson's alternative inscription of 'DOWN WITH SKOOL' was rejected as far too general and unspecific a slogan to suit Richard's case and in the end a compromise was hit upon. 'SECONDARY MODERNS ARE A BLODY SWINDELL, ROLL ON COMPREHENSIVIZATION!' even though this obviously entailed slightly altering and from a dramatic point of view somewhat weakening Mr Howells' response to the carving.

However, as Johnson said, it was a small point compared with the problem of Kipling's general portrayal of Mr Howells.

'You do realize, Kipling, that most people are actually non-graduates? They won't much like being characterised as creeps with no dress sense and their eyes too close together. Debbie's a non-graduate. Her eyes aren't close together. And Alan.'

'Thank you, I see your point fully. That would have been a major blunder of taste – but how shall I get across the point that Howells unwittingly gives various as it were visual clues to his essential lack of qualification to teach Richard decently? Can I keep the idea in at all?'

'Sure. Why not say his shoes and things showed him clearly to be a very decent kindly man but one who did not know a lot about World War One or anything else much in the history line? Cut out false *bonhomie*, narrow eyes etc., and put nice things in.'

'I see.' Kipling wrote for a minute or two. 'Like this perhaps?'

Mr Howells was young, good looking and tastefully dressed in a brown suit, dark tan shoes and crisp white shirt. But there was something about him, despite the genuine sincerity of his smile, the discreet good taste of his dress, despite his honest blue eyes and firm handshake, something that suggested a lack of depth of historical understanding.

'Yes, good,' said Johnson. 'But hang about, what could that something be? What about "a slight twitch at the outer corner of his left eye suggested a lack of true historical understanding." OK?'

So it was decided, and decided moreover with the speed and the lack of petulance or obstinacy on either side which now normally characterized the two men's co-operation.

A True Beginning

I was not present in person in the next crucial stage in the development of the partnership of Kipling and Johnson. Happily though, most of the manuscript drafts of the small passage of *Grey Journey* which led to this very significant shift have survived, and from them a little can be guessed at. To make even a guess, however, requires the skills of the literary historian, for both Kipling and Johnson were always oddly evasive, to my mind, about the circumstances surrounding the composition of this brief passage of the novel and the subtle change in their working relationship which followed.

The passage itself is extremely short and concerns merely Paul's summer holidays of the year 1954 and his translation after the summer break into the same form as his new friend, Stephen Brook.

The first draft read as follows:

The rest of that term, and the summer holiday, passed in a golden haze. The French and Vietminh signed an armistice in Indo China but Paul took little heed of such things, as childhood days raced by.

On 16 September he went back to school, found himself in Form 4A and seated to his joy, right next to the slim dark-haired, dark-eyed boy, Stephen Brook.

The second draft possessed to my mind more bite.

The rest of term and the summer holiday passed in a golden haze. The signing of the Franco-Vietminh armistice gave keen pleasure to Paul and indeed to all his family except Uncle Ted, who feared that the removal of the iron discipline of war from the people of Indo-China might lead them into some kind of moral laxity but that disagreement was the only ripple on the tranquil surface of that summer. On 15 September the All-China People's Congress assembled in Peking and on the next day, the new Grammar School year began. Paul found himself, to his pleasure, in the same form as Stephen Brook, sitting in fact, only a few places from him. He noted that Stephen had put on a good deal of weight during the holiday, and was now best described as stocky rather than slim.

The third draft embodies some radical changes to the final two sentences:

. . . the new grammar school year began and Paul was unmoved to find himself in the same form as Stephen Brook (or Steve as he now liked to be called). Stephen's appearance and demeanour had changed somewhat over the holidays. He had put on several stones in weight and he now resembled a frog in general outline. His face was pockmarked, his eyes bloodshot and he had dyed his hair red. His first words to Paul were, 'Let's go down town at dinner time and look out some crumpet!'

A fourth draft is completely different in structure:

After a ghastly summer cooped up in their slum hovel with his appalling family and their mangy dogs, Paul was in a foul mood as school re-assembled on 16 September. He gained some relief for his feelings at playtime by beating Stephen Brook to a pulp with a length of lead pipe. The years sped by and suddenly it was 1960 and Paul left school.'

One can only guess at the volcanic creative processes and interactions with Johnson, which led from the idyllic tone of the first draft to the almost Jacobean intensity of the fourth, a movement from Delius to Berlioz, from *As You Like It* to *Lear*.

The mystery is compounded by the low-key, very brief nature of the actual final published version.

After the summer holidays Paul was pleased to find himself in the same form as Stephen Brook.

One possible tenuous clue is provided in the final novel of the trilogy, *Quiet Tiger*. In *Quiet Tiger* Paul, now established in London, has an intense but brief relationship with a girl named Yvette, who in Chapter Three is described as a petite, dark-eyed French *au pair* girl. In Chapter Five, the girl is called Yvonne, described as ash blonde and willowy, the daughter of a Scottish MP. All the textual evidence points to Yvonne/Yvette being one and the same person. Yvonne, for instance, in Chapter Five talks explicitly to Paul about their intimate shared experiences of Chapter Three.

All Kipling would ever say about this matter of Yvonne/Yvette was to claim, jokingly, that he had muddled his card-index of characters and at the proof-reading stage the error had 'just slipped through'. Nobody, however, was taken in for a moment by this teasing on Kipling's part, and one of the features of *Quiet Tiger* which has given rise to most bitter disputes of interpretation between the critics is precisely this question of the meaning and import of the transposition (or transformation?) of Yvette/Yvonne. Could it be that in the major change in appearance undergone by Stephen Brook in the discarded third draft of this scene for *Grey Journey* we are seeing the first tentative move towards a Merlin-like toying with reality and with the readers' preconceptions about reality which was to flower fully in the Yvette/Yvonne episode in *Quiet Tiger*?

We can never finally know. What I do know for certain, however, is that it was at this very time that Kipling and Johnson agreed that Kipling henceforth would write unaided the, as it were, linking passages of the narrative, consulting Johnson only on the setpiece scenes. Whatever it was that went on during the writing and re-writing of that (in the published version) tiny and innocuous passage about the summer of 1954 it obviously marked a major step forward in the growth of Kipling's self-confidence and autonomy as an artist, a true beginning indeed.

A 'set piece', as it happened, was required almost immediately. It was obviously necessary for the Paul-Stephen relationship to develop and for some feeling to be generated of Paul's two worlds, home and grammar school coming into collision.

Johnson's suggestion was that the matter was best handled by traditional means, that is to have Paul invited to tea by Stephen's parents. Kipling's reaction was immediate and negative. 'A morass,' he said, 'of clichés. Working class boy uses wrong knife and/or fork, blushes, stammers, drops things, is snubbed; is patronized; inadvertently sits on and breaks priceless old gramophone record of Caruso in "Martha".'

'Where's that one from?'

'That one occurs in Balmer's *The Paws of Poverty* – boy is tongue-tied, is sick, faints – and one case, in Dent's *From Quarrylad to Queens' College, Cambridge*, actually dies of embarrassment!'

'How did he get to Cambridge then?'

'I think it was his brother who died, but you take my general meaning?'

'Oh, yes. But look, these Brook people are compassionate, sensitive left-wingers. What if they laid on a meal of black puddings and things for Paul, to make him feel at home? With the knives and forks clearly labelled, all breakable objets d'art and gramophone records carefully removed – perhaps they could even scatter handfuls of coal dust and general grot around the house, so he feels really at home and relaxed?'

'I think a child of Paul's sensitivity would see through such a charade and so be doubly mortified, embarrassed and so on.'

'Well, why not have an ordinary high tea, with Paul coping quite nicely – no embarrassments etc?'

'I had thought of that. Then it struck me that if no upsetting incidents occurred I would be hard pressed for any means of keeping the scene moving at all, the progress of a high tea in itself, being undramatic to a degree. So I would have to fall back on dialogue, involving the development of several potentially difficult new characters that is, the Brook family. So for tactical as well as artistic reasons, I have decided to continue the policy of breaking with tradition. Stephen will visit Paul's family, and undergo social humiliation. The biter bit, you see. I have roughed out a draft, actually.'

The first draft read as follows:

> So it came about that as the US Senate, on that raw December day, prepared its solemn condemnation of one of its members, one Joseph McCarthy of Wisconsin, Stephen Brook prepared himself to meet the Kane family.
>
> 'Gosh,' he muttered to Paul as the two boys reached Alma Terrace, 'real cobblestones! We've nothing like this at home! And look at the grime everywhere! Even the fog seems more oppressive here! My people's good works and socialist solidarity and so on seem so tawdry and in a sense cheap, compared with this actuality of urban working class experience which you clearly take quite for granted!'
>
> 'I suppose it has a sort of Zolaesque quality,' replied Paul airily. 'But when tha's born to it, tha' pays it little heed.'
>
> Stephen felt his stomach constrict with nervousness.

They reached Number 12, went in.

'Hallo mam, this 'ere's Stephen,' piped Paul.

'Tha's welcome enough lad,' said Elsie. 'So long as tha' frames thisen.'

'I shall indeed frame my sen to the very best of my ability, Mrs Kane!' cried Stephen heartily and blushed scarlet as Elsie gave him a look that left him in no doubt that whatever it was he had said, it had not been the right thing.

'Get that down thee,' said Elsie, pushing a plate of warmed-over fish-cake and greasy chips towards Stephen. He began to eat, grateful for the distraction. There was a chilly silence. He stopped eating.

'Tha's supposed to put HP sauce on it, and then fold your chips into a sandwich with the bread like this,' whispered Paul.

Stephen smiled wanly and began with trembling hands to make an unskilful sauce-smeared sandwich with his chips.

The door flew open. 'Is t'soddin tea on t'table, lass?' boomed the coal-grimed Alf Kane.

'Ay, where's tea mam?' echoed Richard, nearly as tall as his father already, and now a coal-grimed collier too.

'And who's this bugger sat in my chair?' Richard pointed a black finger at the cringing Stephen.

'Oh please have your chair,' cried Stephen leaping to his feet. 'I do not wish to be a nuisance! Perhaps one of the servants could make up a tray and Paul and I could retire to the drawing-room?' He realized his ghastly blunder as soon as the words passed his lips. 'Gosh! Silly of me. Typically bourgeois insensitivity to the actuality of working-class housing conditions!'

'Sit on t'sofa Stephen,' said Elsie, in a voice of ice.

'Daft bugger,' sniggered Richard.

The rest of the meal passed in a rather awkward silence.

'Brilliant conception!' was Johnson's comment. 'But carry it on a bit. Stephen needs to meet the dogs, remember. They are ultimately the reason for Stephen's being there at all.' Kipling duly extended the passage:

Suddenly Stephen felt a movement under the dusty sofa. It was Rex. Rex pushed his black nose inquisitively against Stephen's ankle and then crawled out, stretching and yawning, from beneath the sofa. Prince followed him, snapping playfully at Rex's stubby brown tail.

'Ooh, doggies!' quavered Stephen. He blushed as everyone in the small room turned their eyes coldly on him.

'We did know they were dogs!' spat Elsie. 'Linguistically and educationally deprived as we be, sithee, we can all recognize dogs as a category tha' knows and can correctly name and identify them as such, by gum.'

'I only meant,' quavered Stephen, 'that I've always longed deeply for the companionship of a dog of my own.' Rex the terrier caught Stephen's eye and nodded sympathetically.

'Why don't tha' get one then?' queried Richard, 'tha's enough brass for two dozen bloody dogs.'

'My mummy has an allergy to fur,' explained Stephen ingratiatingly. The room fell bleakly silent again.

'I'm sorry!' stammered Stephen, 'the locution "mummy" must of course be deeply offensive to you, I only meant . . .'

'No, no,' interrupted Paul helpfully, 'the thing is, tha' sees, we can't afford ailments such as allergies, round here, nobbut simple stuff such as bronchitis and appropriate industrial diseases.'

'Aye!' boomed Alfred, 'we mek do wi' measles and scarlatina and such, i'childhood. Then we graduate to TB, silicosis, emphysema. Allergies are not for the like of us, nor neuroses neither. Nor yet hormonal imbalance, nor feelin's of insecurity nor inadequacy. Nowt posh at all. Nowt', he scowled savagely.

'We're allowed VD,' sniggered Richard.

'Shut thy filthy gob!' cried Alf and smashed Richard, bleeding, to the floor with a blow of his huge forearm. Prince, Richard's dog to the core, flew into action. Pausing only to bite Alf forcefully in the calf he rushed to the prostrate Richard and began furiously to lick the youth's face.

'Tha' mun forgive our simple ways, Stephen,' muttered Alf. 'Chuck a bucket o' watter o'er t'lad, Elsie, to fetch 'im around. And convey my apologies to 'im, when his senses return, like. And while tha's at it, fetch a bit of shirt tail or summat to wrap round this bite i' my leg. Now then, sithee, 'ave a pot o' tea, young Stephen.'

Alf's well meant attempt to smooth things over, however, was quite lost on young Stephen Brook. He was thinking how he would not in the least mind lying unconscious, bleeding slightly from the mouth, if he could be licked adoringly by a dog such as Prince. Or Rex.

Afterwards, Paul walked with Stephen to the corner of Alma Terrace. 'Basically', explained Paul, 'they're shy, sithee, in t' t'presence o' strangers. Hence their outwardly brusque manner. But if you want to come again . . .'

'Oh, yes, please,' cried Stephen eagerly, somewhat to Paul's surprise. 'And could you,' stammered Stephen, 'could you give Rex and Prince one of these each? – I would have liked to give them myself but I wasn't awfully sure of the protocol.' He took out of his pocket, and shyly offered to Paul, two cold chips.

Paul talked about the visit, later, to Uncle Ted.

'It were as if two different worlds were trying to communicate, Uncle,' he explained, 'two worlds using a language outwardly common to both, but wi' resonances and sub-texts so differently interpreted by the two parties as not merely to hinder communication, but virtually to prevent it. Sithee. What does it all mean, Uncle?'

'It means,' rejoined Uncle Ted, 'that tha's coming to a time when tha'll have to choose, Paul. Choose, select, take sides, decide which world is truly thine, which side tha' rightly belongs to, which way tha'll go at moment o' choosin' and decision.'

'I think I tek thy meaning, Uncle,' replied Paul, troubled.

'Terrific,' was Johnson's comment. 'Now all you have to do is arrange for Paul to meet and fall in love with Ailsa and the whole thing is set up.'

'Oh, I've dealt with that already,' said Kipling. 'Not as a setpiece, merely *en passant*. I remembered your interesting remark about that strange fifties custom of sisters distributing sweets to provincial grammar school boys and worked the idea in. Would you like to hear it, for interest? I'll read it out.'

As the autumn of 1954 dipped towards winter, Paul found himself almost unconsciously looking forward more and more keenly to Ailsa's visits to the school. On Tuesdays and Thursdays, during the mid-morning breaks, she would ride her cobby little grey pony Toby into the school-yard and distribute sweets, sherbet or chocolate to her brother Stephen and his friends. To Ailsa in the dignity of her sixteen summers, Paul was just one more pair of grubby hands, reaching for a Kit-Kat or a jellybaby. To Paul, though, Ailsa's neat black hair and dark eyes, her exquisitely cut khaki jodhpurs, black jacket and pertly set black riding helmet began slowly but surely to become the stuff of dreams.

'OK?'

'Yes, great,' said Johnson not very warmly. 'Super. I think.'

'I can see that you have a reservation,' said Kipling, 'and I believe I know what it is. Why is Ailsa Brook herself not at school, you are wondering? Well, she is being educated at home, largely by her mother – who is a woman of parts as Stephen Brook has earlier made clear – because she is handicapped. More specifically she is deaf. Thus any extended dialogue with Paul is ruled out physically as well as by the age-gap and social gulf. She will always remain utterly aloof, unattainable.'

'Great. Super,' said Johnson. 'Wait a bit, though. He could write to her, couldn't he?'

'Yes. No. Wait a moment – what a splendid idea. He could write letters to Ailsa revealing his inmost thoughts, emotions, and so on. Letters which are *never sent*, of course. But they could speed the plot along excellently – rather like the snapshot idea. I think I will try one out and see how it reads. . .

8 Jan. 1955. My darling Ailsa, How I long to see you ride into the school yard on Toby once again, sithee, distributing Maltesers or Pontefract cakes. I think a great deal about you, notwithstanding, tha' knows, that at some level I recognize that my feelings for you are but adolescent 'puppy-love' as it is vulgarly known, sithee. But darker things are on my mind too. All of us wonder what is portended by t'replacement of Mr Malenkov by this man Bulganin as t'Soviet head of state, but my own mind is greatly exercised currently, sithee, by t'question of t'existence or otherwise of a personal God. Stephen tends towards a mechanistic materialism, I know, and at t'other Pole, as it were, my Uncle Ted envisages a highly personal and somewhat vengeful Deity, quite close to the Old Testament model. For mysel', like, I'm toying with the notion of immanence, tainted though it be with spineless Pantheism (vide Wordsworth) I would be glad to hear your views on this matter, by gum, and I love you insanely I would kill myself for you, should you so require,

Yours faithfully,
Paul Kane'

'It's got something,' was Johnson's comment on this text. 'But what's all this "sithee" bit?'

'Of course!' Kipling almost shouted. 'Paul would not *write* in that confounded dialect! He would write good, plain, standard English! How very stupid of me. But what a release! And what a good further reason for persevering with the letter technique, if it can be made to work, that is. What do you think?'

'Well, this one is very moving, but it doesn't get the plot forward much. Can he use the letters to describe events, do you think?'

'I could try. What events had you in mind?'

'Well, say, the school play. Sports day. Somebody could let stink-bombs off in a chemistry lesson.'

'Rather thin, I think, as plot mechanisms.'

'Yes – actually nothing much does happen at school, come to think, not once you're about thirteen, does it? What about a disaster at the mine then?'

'We could only do that once. And such violent plot devices are exactly what you yourself have often warned me forcefully against.'

'OK. No explosions until we really need one, then. Wait a bit. Paul hasn't got the full school uniform has he? What if he gradually gets bits, and each bit is charged with significance and linked with the history of his time, e.g. the school blazer symbolizes the H-bomb. And a new satchel, a proper leather one, could symbolize affluence under Macmillan. No? When can he leave for university then?'

'1960,' said Kipling gloomily.

'And what is it now?'

'1955. January.'

'I think this might be what writers call a block.'

I made them some tea.

'Have you got a Bible or complete works of Shakespeare?' asked Johnson after a prolonged and gloomy interval.

'A Shakespeare, certainly, over there – but why?'

'Well, I saw this film once about a blocked writer and

what he did was open the Bible or Shakespeare at random and try to get unblocking ideas from the first line on the page.'

'Did it work?'

'No, but we've nothing else to do, have we? – So here goes.' Johnson opened the Complete Works at random and discovered this passage.

Merchant of Venice, Act 5, Scene 1.
A kind of boy, a little scrubbed boy
No higher than myself, the judge's clerk.

'How if,' said Johnson, 'There's this little kid who was very small. And Paul thumps him, to keep his hand in at bullying and he dies i.e. the little boy does, and Paul gets a stretch in Borstal. From the judge, you see? No? Let's try again. What about this bit?'

As You Like It, Act 4, Scene 1
'I prithee pretty youth, let me be better acquainted with thee.'

'Scrub that. One more go?'

'I don't feel,' said Kipling, 'that we are approaching all this in quite the right way.'

'You're right. Thinks. Look, remember we used World War Two to get the whole thing started – can we unblock with a bit of history now, do you think. Was there any history going on in 1955?'

'Not really. But wait a moment, in 1956 there were Suez and Hungary!'

'Suez! Terrific. Work in the impact of the Suez Crisis and Hungary on the life of Paul Kane and vice versa!'

'I'll try,' said Kipling. Hope re-kindled, a little. Kipling stuck to his newly discovered 'letters' mode for his first essay at the critical Suez-Hungary episode.

31 October 1956

My dearest Ailsa,

There are dark times indeed. Our love seems such a frail barque on the stormy seas of our times, especially as we cannot yet be said to have, properly speaking, spoken to one another, your deafness and my shyness restricting our contact to smiles which on my side are freighted with desperate meaning and on yours – who knows?

The Soviets have invaded Hungary, and brought down a generation of socialist idealism in ruins. We are invading Egypt and may bring down – who can say? Perhaps civilization itself. And the worst thing for me is the impatience I feel with the reactions of my family to it all. How irritating, for example, is my mother's habit of outlining quite cogently the bleak facts of the case or cases, and then in typical left-liberal style presenting no recommendation!

My father's vigorous attribution of all ills to the working of the international boss-class which for some time has been striking me as quaintly dated now appears to me positively tiresome – I almost prefer brother Richard's position, namely that they are all just wogs and had it coming to them, whoever they are. This view has at least the supreme merit of simplicity.

That cannot alas be said of Uncle Ted's stance. His revelation to me that the Egyptians and Hungarians are of a common racial stock and that the Hungarians are none other than the Amalekites of the Old Testament was interesting but his conclusion that we should pray for the speedy destruction of the Egyptian race, and then as our Christian duty resettle the Hungarians by the Nile banks seemed to me, frankly, poorly argued.

How restless and dissatisfied I feel, how grey and restricted, how provincial it is here! And yet . . . I love you with unutterable passion,

Yours sincerely
Paul Kane.

'It's great,' said Johnson, 'But I think it could be a much bigger thing, you know, a big key scene I think he really should go to lunch with the Brooks. There's something for them to talk about now, i.e. Suez and things. So Paul could meet a whole new lot of ideas excitingly in a natural way. He could write a letter to Ailsa about it afterwards if you like.'

'Well I could do it, I suppose. It would form a counterpoint to Stephen's visit to Alma Terrace and at least I can drop dialect – I presume that Paul would be speaking reasonable English by 1956. It might after all be a good scene, possibly.'

'There is another thing,' said Johnson hesitantly. 'You won't like this. I know you won't like this. That's why I've not mentioned it sooner. But I think you ought to think about it. Right? OK. You want to get this published, right? OK. Well, I was reading in the paper the other week that the chances for a new, unknown novelist of getting published these days are about zilch. What they need to publish to make any money is cookery books and books about gardening. Recipes and gardening tips, they can shift, this article said, but novels, nix. Pure economics.'

'That's very discouraging news, certainly, but what can I do about it except go on writing and hope for the best?'

'Put recipes and gardening hints in the story as they come up, naturally.'

'Are you,' asked Kipling, 'raving mad?'

'No. Look. What's the use of writing the greatest novel since ever if nobody reads it?'

'Not a great deal I admit. But equally, what is the point of trying to pass off a book of recipes and gardening hints as a novel? Artistic integrity may sometimes have to be slightly compromised in the name of commerce, I grant you, but a recipe-book!'

'Not a recipe book. Recipes and gardening tips. A few. Just to give you that extra edge with publishers' readers. Look, Paul Kane meets the *famille* Brook – what more natural than that their strange middle-class food and their middle-class garden should attract his restless intellectual curiosity? And lots of people write about food. Virginia Woolf goes on and on about a *Boeuf en daube* in one of her books, I think. And gardens! Wow, people in novels are always fooling about in gardens, thinking, and committing suicide and screwing each other etc. What's so wrong with being the first English novelist to actually tell people something useful about food and gardens while you're at it? And guaranteeing getting published at the same time.'

'No.'

'Why not just try a draft? What's to lose?'

'My self-respect as an artist is what there is to lose. However under protest and purely for the sake of your unstinting help, you understand, in the past, I will try a short passage. Purely to show you that it will not work.'

Thus unwillingly, indeed under protest, Peter Kipling found that last element required to give his work its unmistakably distinctive character, that element described by the anonymous critic of *The Times Literary Supplement* as 'a quiddity, a *sui generis* mode of being English, of England. Mere gardening hints and recipes on the surface, but they give the book a direct relationship to experienced reality, a strength like the gnarled and ramifying roots of an old oak-tree, struck deep into the very clays, gravels and loams of English provincial life'. In truth, for Kipling the artist, this casual and unwilling decision marked the end of the beginning.

The End of the Beginning

Stephen's stocky grey-haired father greeted Paul at the door of Park Knoll.

'Come in, my boy, come in,' he cried heartily, 'nippy outside these early November days, but the ideal time for moving the larger shrubs, you know. Make sure the leaves have all dropped, then your shrub won't suffer any unnecessary moisture loss in its new situation.'

'And remember to spread the roots and fork in a good supply of peat as you bed the shrub into its new home.' The new speaker was Mrs Brook, a tall, slender, dark-haired woman wearing a simple but elegant grey twin-set and flat heeled light tan shoes. 'You must be Paul,' murmured Mrs Brook, smiling.

'Yes indeed,' replied Paul, 'and thank you for your valuable hints on the moving of shrubs. Of course I cannot apply them immediately since we have no gardens in Alma Terrace, merely squalid back-yards and front doors that go straight onto the street.'

'Of course,' muttered Mr Brook colouring and nervously fingering one of the three buttons on his fawn sports coat. 'Stupid of us. Unimaginative, to say the least.'

'Pray do not feel embarrassed on my account,' said Paul and led the way into the dining-room.

'You could have small pot-plants at home, though!' cried Mrs Brook brightly, trying to make up for the gaffe. 'If you do, be careful not to over-water them and consult the nurseryman about exactly where to stand them. They vary greatly in their liking for warmth and sunlight.'

Stephen joined them. 'Hullo Paul,' he said. He seemed oddly subdued.

The lunch began with avocado pears, a huge novelty for Paul, eaten with silver Apostle spoons. Stuffed chicken followed.

'I would be interested,' ejaculated Paul, 'to hear the views of middle-class intellectual socialists such as yourselves on the Suez and Hungary affairs and compare them with those of my family whose political sympathies are broadly similar but rooted in very different social experiences.'

'Jolly straightforward, the Suez business, really!' cried Mr Brook. 'Quite unsubtle piece of old-fashioned imperialism but rendered popular even across party lines by its very straightforwardness and spurious appearance of decisiveness.'

'And also,' added Mrs Brook, 'the canal is a very potent symbol to British people who imagine, for instance, that the Desert War of 1941–43 was fought to preserve it from falling into German hands. So what more natural than to strive to preserve it again?'

'Ay,' cried Paul, 'a popular belief nonetheless precious for being quite an inaccurate assessment of the role of the Canal in World War II!'

'Yes,' said Mr Brook with a strange edge to his tone, 'the British people think they know all about the geopolitics of the Near East. Hungary on the other hand . . .'

'I don't think Paul wants to know about Hungary,' said Mrs Brook quickly. 'I'm sure he would rather know the recipe for this chicken stuffing, wouldn't you?' Paul was not slow to take a hint.

'Yes, please,' he cried merrily, 'let me take it down on a bit of paper.' Mrs Brook dictated:

'4 chicken livers
¾lb mushrooms sautéed in butter. Handful of fresh breadcrumbs.
2 rashers of bacon
3 shallots
a clove of garlic
salt, pepper and parsley
2 eggs

She paused for what seemed to Paul a long time. The thin November sunlight streamed into the room, playing on the polished floorboards, the elegant ladder-back chairs, the dense whiteness of the table-cloth. There was an uneasy silence.

'– a sprinkling of Hungarian Paprika.'
Mrs Brook finished the recipe.

'Thank you,' said Paul, quietly. People began to eat again, making a little more noise than strictly necessary with their knives and forks. The atmosphere slowly relaxed and the conversation turned to poetry, Paul telling them of the enthusiasm for Dryden and Pope which he had picked up from Uncle Ted, the Brooks talking incisively yet sensitively of Keats and Wordsworth.

'Grapes under the grill' followed the chicken (*made*

131

from 1lb of Cyprus grapes, 1½ gills of cream and 2 tablespoons of Barbados sugar). The talk gaily swung to music. The Brooks enchanted Paul with their knowledgeable enthusiasm for Beethoven and Puccini. Paul contributed shyly when he could, talking of his love for Corelli, Telemann and Geminiani.

It was with sinking heart that Paul finally set out for home, turning his back on this world of light and elegance, music and poetry, turning back towards Alma Terrace. Stephen came to the gate of Park Knoll with him.

'Why did they seem not to want to talk about Hungary, Steve?' asked Paul curiously.

Stephen looked pale and tense. 'They've quarrelled over Hungary. Mummy sees the Soviet action as a justified riposte to counter-revolution. Daddy, *au contraire*, says its just old-style Stalinist *real-politik*. He's going to leave the CP I think,' his lip trembled. 'I think they might get divorced.'

Paul stood at a loss. 'I hope everything – well – give them this – I was going to, but I felt a bit silly. Here.' He ran off into the gathering gloom leaving Stephen holding a small piece of paper, bearing Paul's spiky, idiosyncratic hand-writing. It said:

'*YORKSHIRE PUDDING*
One egg
3 oz flour
3 fl. oz milk
2 fl. oz water
Salt and pepper
2 tablespoons beef dripping
Preheat oven to gas mark 7.'

'What do you think?' asked Kipling.

'Terrific – but it's really a matter of what you think yourself, this time.'

'Actually in this particular case, I thought the effect of the recipes and so on, especially the pathos of the Yorkshire Pudding recipe not at all bad. Worth persevering with I think. I must admit, my initial hostility was perhaps an over-reaction.'

'Great. I thought it was bang on – just one thing – where's Ailsa and her sister, thingy?'

'Goodness yes. An oversight. Look, could I just have someone say "What a pity the girls can't be here" and leave it at that? Apart from anything else the stuffing and grapes recipes are for four people and I am not sure how to multiply them up to recipes for six.'

'Good thinking. Hey, what if the girls have already split as it were, in a big way – Ailsa, say has gone to join the Israeli Army in Sinai and thingy is joining the Hungarian freedom fighters etc.'

'I don't think the Israeli army would have taken Ailsa. She was profoundly deaf, you recall.'

'Perhaps the Hungarians would then – they were very hard up for manpower etc. weren't they?'

'I think to avoid complications I will just have the girls discreetly absent,' said Kipling firmly. 'But I do think that taking the focus briefly away from the world of Paul and the Brooks could be useful. I think I will try a little counterpoint passage about brother Richard, again, and see if recipes and so on can be at all useful there.'

Richard's lunchtime had been different in tone. He had spent it drinking in the 'Royal Oak', and at 1.35 p.m. found himself hitting a total stranger on the back of the head with a beer tankard. Somebody then hit Richard a sickening blow in the ribs. Glasses flew, and boots and oaths. Police whistles. Richard and his friends ran for it. They fetched up at the old railway bridge, retching, panting, clutching assorted bruised and bloodied limbs and laughing helplessly.

'What were all that about for Christ's sake? Who the fuck were that bugger I belted?' gasped Richard, between sobs of laughter.

'Were it about Suez Canal or summat?'

'Nay sithee,' said young Alan Bennett, gingerly

fingering his swollen jaw. 'It were yon daft old bugger Ellis. He were mekkin' out that tha' can grow shallots from seed. That Scotch feller were sayin' that they bolt easy grown from seed and that its better by far, sithee, to set out bulbs in an open sunny position in early March, some 6 to 8 inches apart wi' about a foot between the rows. He were right tha' knows but owld Ellis belted him, so 'e belted Ellis, so thou belted t'Scotch bloke wi' thy tankard.' They laughed, helplessly.

'I've had eight pints,' said Richard, solemnly, sinking to a sitting position against the soot-soaked parapet of the old railway bridge. 'Eight soddin' pints.'

'I'm not sure,' said Johnson, 'that you need any more help from me. This novel's going like a runaway train, I think.'

'You do yourself too little justice,' said Kipling, but I could see he was pleased.

The next highlight in Paul's story, however, led to a little more friction between the collaborators, with an interesting outcome.

A few days after the lunch at the Brooks' house, Paul is surprised to find himself invited again to the Brooks, this time to tea . . .

Delicious *pâté* sandwiches, served on Napoleon Ivy pattern plates, were followed by a chocolate layer cake. Stephen seemed in surprisingly good spirits.

'How are, er, things?' queried Paul cautiously.'

'Oh, things,' merrily replied Stephen, 'are not too bad, actually, things are, and talking of things, there's a present for you, over here.'

He quickly removed the wrapping paper from a large object, standing on the floor near the William Morris tiled fireplace. It was a large plant pot containing a small shrub, some twelve inches high. 'It is a fuchsia,' murmured Mrs Brook from the doorway of the dining-room. She was wearing a black skirt, black knitted sleeveless cardigan over a red blouse and medium height black court shoes. She went on:

'It is a Fuchsia Cottinghamii. It will grow nicely in its pot in your back yard. It is reasonably hardy and not too fussy about sunlight, but bring it indoors during the season of hard frost. Keep it well watered.'

'Thank you very much,' replied Paul. 'You are very kind and very generous. I also noticed that the *pâté* was home made. My palate is, of course, accustomed only to fish cakes and black pudding and the like, but even I could tell that. I would guess that the *pâté* had been composed roughly as follows:

4tbl. well chopped onion, 1oz butter, ¼ pint Madeira, ¾lb each of finely minced lean veal and lean pork, 2 eggs, 1½ tsp. salt, a pinch of pepper, ½tsp. thyme. Am I correct?'

'There was a clove of garlic as well,' murmured Mrs Brook. 'Perhaps I should explain,' she went on, 'we all feel that we owe you a great debt. On Sunday when Stephen gave us your Yorkshire Pudding recipe we felt that the simple northern working-class directness of your gesture was a rebuke to our own convoluted, and, at bottom, largely semantic squabbles about neo-Stalinism, the precise socio-political thrust of late capitalism, the vanguard role of the proletariat, revisionism, labourism.'

'Neo-colonialism!' chimed in Stephen, eagerly, 'and the significance of the Soviets' 20th Party Congress . . .'

'And I expect you've also been giving much fundamentally profitless thought to the concept of embourgeoisiement and whether any distinct meaning can be attached to the label "Maoist",' said Paul encouragingly.

'Yes, yes all those things,' cried Mrs Brook. 'But when we met you and somehow especially when you gave us the Yorkshire Pudding recipe, we saw it all for what it was – words! Self-indulgent Hampstead outpourings! So we are all going to stay together and join the Labour Party, and work with what is to hand, with the tools that are to hand! Here in Mexthorpe! And we owe this cleansing and re-vivifying insight to you in conjunction, of course, with the disturbing events in Hungary and Egypt.'

Paul was a little taken aback. The truth was, that he himself had latterly been drifting away from that very labourite reformism now evidently so enthusiastically embraced by the Brooks, towards a position both individualist and revolutionary, best described as anarchist.

'Fifty men own the lemon grove, and no man is a slave.' That fiery line it was which currently excited his young imagination, its hints of harsh Spanish sunlight, of the smell of cordite and sweat on a Civil War battlefield dazzled the mind and gave a drab, worn and dog-eared look to all less romantic versions of left politics.

'I'm glad to hear of your decision, very glad,' Paul cried.

He had learned to dissimulate. The bright world of the Brooks which a few days ago had seemed to him to have the perfect, brilliant yet intimate charm of a seventeenth-century Netherlands interior he now knew to have its own flaws, its own moral equivalent of worn patches of carpet.

This realization on Paul's part coincided broadly with the entry of Russian tanks into Budapest and precisely with the deaths of two young Hungarian boys of Paul's own age. They had conceived the idea of ramming an iron bar gainst the tracks of a Soviet tank, to immobilize it. The idea was not in itself a bad one, and might well have worked, had they not been cut down by machine gun bullets from tank 'A' some yards short of their target, which we might call tank 'B'. Thus, as Paul learned that day a little about moral ambiguity, Gregor and Sandor learned the hard way that tank commanders work in pairs.

The fuchsia survived the winter and flowered well the

next spring.

Johnson's general comments were respectful to the point of awe.

'Just one tiny thing – do you think Paul would have figured out the *pâté* recipe quite so precisely, just from tasting the *pâté* itself?'

'That is a real difficulty. I had thought of Paul saying "onions, veal and that sort of thing," but that hardly amounts to a recipe, does it?'

'Why can't Mrs Brook just tell Paul the recipe?'

'Because the point of the *pâté* episode is that Paul has the insight to work out for himself that Mrs Brook has asked him round for some special reason and at such a moment, a boy of that sensitivity would hardly ask for a *pâté* recipe. Why, indeed, would he wish to know it? Likewise, Mrs Brook is, I think, unlikely to offer him a *pâté* recipe at such a charged point in time. No, it must come from Paul.'

'Could he not offer a sort of alternative, working-class type *pâté* recipe – maybe with tripe and things?'

'Since Mrs Brook and her entire family have already perceived the Yorkshire Pudding recipe as an unintended but sharp rebuke to their whole way of life, yet another down-to-earth Yorkshire recipe, at this tense moment would obviously reduce the poor woman to actual tears of shame and remorse.'

'Well, could he at least look at the *pâté* with a magnifying glass and sort of poke it as he figures out the recipe? Like Sherlock Holmes.'

'That would surely sound absurd? "Paul produced a pocket magnifying glass and teased apart the crumbs of *pâté*, rapidly identifying 4 tbl. of well-chopped onion etc." Ridiculous, surely?'

'Oh, all right, leave it as it stands,' said Johnson. But there was a trace of petulance in his tone, and I do not believe that he was fully persuaded of the merit of Kipling's decision. The balance of power between the two had clearly tilted further in Kipling's direction, as his creative force matured and his confidence burgeoned accordingly.

The Way Ahead

The next major episode was the opening of the celebrated Lakeland passage. Kipling offered it to Johnson for comment in draft without preamble.

On 15 August 1958, the day King Hussein dissolved the Federation of Jordan and Iraq, Paul Kane and Stephen Brook were approaching the Derwentwater Youth Hostel in the evening, quite unaware of this latest twist in the history of the Fertile Crescent. Falcon Crag was still pooled in sunshine, as if part of another day and another place while to the west the Derwent Falls humped stolidly over the lake were beginning to shade from slate-grey to purple as the sun edged behind Dale Head. The boys stood in silence for a moment. Paul was wearing a plain grey shirt and brown cord shorts with an old leather Boy Scout belt. He carried a khaki ex-army back-pack by way of a rucksack. Stephen wore a khaki drill shirt and shorts, and cleated walking boots. He carried a green canvas rucksack.

'I think,' opined Paul, 'that to offer verbal comment on the scene before us would be superfluous and in a sense tasteless.'

'I heartily concur,' replied Stephen. 'But a written attempt to capture the moment, perhaps by way of a poem, might be fitting. The moment being, to coin a phrase, recollected in tranquillity.'

'But,' demurred Paul, 'surely such an attempt would be doomed to derivativeness, if not, outright banality? The Romantics have surely ploughed this particular soil until it will yield no more?'

The discussion had brought them to the Youth Hostel door and the next minutes were full of the bustle of unpacking and starting to cook a meal.

Stephen tipped in a tin of soup.

'Possibly,' he said as he stirred, 'you are right. But perhaps any artistic endeavour however banal is worthwhile, if it represents a sincere attempt to communicate a vision. Perhaps our restless search for novelty as such is misguided?'

'Maybe so,' returned Paul, thoughtfully. 'After all, the Orientals saw nothing wrong in endlessly painting and repainting the landscape of Kweichow, or Mount Fuji.'

'And to take a homelier example,' returned Stephen. 'Every year between January and mid-March my father prunes his roses, cutting them back just above a dormant shoot bud pointing away from the centre of the plant and not more than six inches from the base. This action could be described as banal, but who would so criticize the resulting well-formed rose bushes and their exquisite summer blooms?'

'I've never tried to write a poem before,' said Paul.

After supper, while Stephen read 'Justine', Paul wrote his first poem in the Notes Section of his pocket diary. Mexthorpe felt very far away as the blunt stub of pencil struggled over the tiny page.

When the untitled poem was done, Paul read it through, again and again.

The Fells!
Their woods and dells!
they speak to me like dulcet bells!
The Lake!
As I awake
It quivers to the sunlight's shake.

Then he initialled it PK. Paul Kane, poet.'

'That's rather fine, I think,' said Johnson. 'Marvellously visual. Just one thing. The Poem. It's not really all that, well, good.'

'Of course not. It's awful. It is Paul's very first effort.'

'Even so. I think at sixteen he would have read a lot of poems. Even a first effort would not sound quite so Eric Thribb, I think.'

'Very well. I will write a better one,' said Kipling, and dashed off the following verses:

The curlews offer poetic punctuation, as
The poet surveys Cumbria, the well-named.
His language-cogs mill and sort 'green' 'grey'
'Uptilt' 'sea-grey sky' but not much
Sifts through onto the page.
The poet's wordcogs seek names for the Fell.
All that they find is 'Big' and 'Cold'
The pen clogs. The poet recalls that
One thing Wordsworth felt, up here, was fear.
It seems a good idea to get back in the car
And drive to somewhere smaller.
The curlews stay. They are here on business.

Johnson greatly preferred the new version of Paul's poem though feeling that it strayed a little too far now in the direction of sophistication and world-weariness. He suggested that the poet, might 'get back on his bike,' not into a car, and that the poem could be ended by two lines both more optimistic and also hinting a little more strongly at the rawness of Paul's poetic talent.

Other bits of Lakeland are not so creepy
And are really very nice if it stays fine.

Long discussion left Kipling still unwilling to concede these alterations but he eagerly took up Johnson's final idea, which was that Paul's lakeland idyll should be counterpointed by a violently contrasting episode from the life of Richard, who was now nineteen and could reasonably be supposed to be a National Serviceman.

Johnson's first idea was to make Richard an army cook, thus giving scope for the convenient introduction of many recipes. It was quickly decided, though, that Richard should actually go to war as an infantry soldier both to provide a more telling contrast with the

Lakeland episode, and because, as Kipling astutely pointed out, there was much more literature available as models for scenes of battle, than there were literary accounts of army catering matters. The first draft read as follows:

Dawn of that same day, 15 August 1958, found Richard Kane very differently placed from his brother. He was slightly seasick and full of a dull, barely controlled fear as his landing craft neared the shores of the island of Adjiba. Adjiba was yet another of the trouble spots which proliferated like political acne in these last days of Empire. Palestine, Aden, Cyprus, Egypt, Adjiba. Always 'troublespots', 'states of emergency', 'police actions'. Never 'wars'. Except people appeared to die, just like in wars, somehow.

The teenaged subaltern, a youth of fresh complexion, medium height and light blue eyes ran through the 'briefing' one last time.

'Right. Now we've got the KRR on the right and KSLI on the left. 'B' Coy. will do a left-flank with MG and 2-inch support, on feature 305. We're doing a straight pepper-pot PIA with F. and M. on point ref. 276 stroke 138. We know the wogs have HMG so there's going to be point 5 as well as 303, incoming. We'll RV for O group and sitrep, at 0615 approx. Any questions?' There were none.

'Ay,' thought Richard cynically, 'it's all crystal bloody clear when tha sits on thy bum here and explains it like that, but wi' real bloody thing, as it were, well, we shall see, 'ow t'best made plans pan out.'

'Real bloody thing' started thirty seconds later as the ramp went down, and Richard and his section plunged into thigh deep, surprisingly warm water and into a hail of machine gun, rifle, mortar and artillery fire of various calibres.

Five seconds after they reached dry land, there was a blinding orange flash. Richard lay flat, clutched the sand briefly in a spasm of fear, and then ran on. He seemed to have lost touch with his section. A tank loomed out of the smoke, moving from left to right at approximately 10 m.p.h. Seconds or minutes later another tank, painted like the first in a dun yellow tone, loomed out of a dust cloud and moved from right to left, as viewed from Richard's position, at a speed nearer to 15 m.p.h.

Bullets apparently of 9mm calibre, suggesting an automatic weapon of some kind, kicked sand near Richard's feet. He saw the man firing at him – it was Bullock of 11 Platoon. 'Friend! Friend!' shrieked Richard. 'Friend!' 'I 'ave no bloody friends' gritted Bullock morosely, but at least he stopped firing. 'Nay,' said Richard 'when a' said "friend" I didn' mean to mek out any soort o' social bond atween us, I nobbut meant a military convention whereby . . .' Before Richard could finish his explanation a hoarse command, rang out 'Platoon! Fix bayonets! Charge.'

Richard attached himself to 11 Platoon and charged. The charge took them to Richard's confused surprise back to the water's edge. 'Fuckin' duff compasses,' gritted the leathery old NCO who had ordered and led the charge. Richard decided to seek out his own platoon and set off along the beach.

He met first a small dusky boy dressed in khaki shirt and shorts and blue sneakers with white piping, who hissed 'Cigarettes, Tommy? You like meet sister?' 'Ay, I'd like to meet thy sister summat champion, by gum, but 'ow is it to be fixed up? I 'ave pressin' military duties . . .' But the youngster was gone, lost in the swirling fog of war. Further along the beach, Richard met a group of cowards, snivelling, and a padre in his early thirties, dark-haired with a sallow complexion, who furnished him with a Senior Service cigarette and a cheery word. Several wounded soliders pressed on him letters to loved ones, a silver gilt crucifix, sundry rosaries and oral messages of various kinds. Horses ran by from time to time, each one with its entrails hanging out.

Richard came at last to a shallow trench where dead British and German soldiers –

'Germans?' interrupted Johnson rather brusquely. 'Sorry. – Careless.'

– where dead British soldiers and, er, foreigners lay face down in the comradeship of death, or in the light of the next bit, perhaps they'd better lie face up – sorry, sorry.

Richard recognized among them a cheery young Cockney, ex-baker's roundsman; a quiet bespectacled youth, former insurance clerk; a lively Welsh boy who had in life, a excellent tenor voice, and a tough, dour but good-hearted former stevedore from Glasgow. None of the dead foreigners of course was known to Richard personally, but he guessed that they probably represented in their turn a similar cross-section of Adjiban society.

'What's it all mean?' he groaned, 'What's it all bloody mean?'

'Now before you comment, could I just run through my check-list, er, 'Bullets (kicking sand etc.) . . . entrails . . . confusion (cf Tolstoy Borodino) and Stendhal (Waterloo) all right . . . padre . . . yes. Welsh boy (tenor). Seems all right. Ah, I've missed out handgrenades (machine gun post knocked out by). Drat.'

'The leathery old NCO with the duff compass could do that,' suggested Johnson.

'Yes. But he's at the water's edge when Richard leaves him, we'd have to take him all the way back up to somewhere or other to do it. And with a faulty compass.'

'How about one of the cowards? One of the cowards stops snivelling for a minute and with a barely human cry of rage and thingy hurls himself towards a machine gun post?'

'Good. I'll use that. Thank you. What about the episode generally?'

'Super. Don't people vomit in war-bits, though?'

'Quite true. Good point. We'll have the cowards snivelling and vomiting as well I think.'

'Well,' said Johnson, tentatively, 'do you think it would also be handy to work in some big noise general, either a sensitive one tormented by the need for bloodshed, or a right sod who only wants a knighthood and doesn't care who gets creamed if he gets it? Also he would sort of echo Wavell in the conception of Paul scene.'

'Perhaps,' murmured Kipling. . .

'Further along the beach Richard met two red-tabbed Generals, one with a sensitive, tormented face, the other cold-eyed and ruthless.'

'No, I think he'd hardly meet two generals in one place, on one beach, I mean. Perhaps we could say "he met a General, but whether the impressive red-tabbed figure had a sensitive, tormented face or the hard cold-eyed looks of a ruthless manipulator of humble men's destinies Richard could not tell, because of the smoke and dust."'

'Good. I'd suggest you tidy that up a bit and keep it in. I suppose it was too tricky to get recipes or gardening tips into this bit?'

'Not really – in fact I planned originally for Richard's platoon to exchange recipes and gardening hints as the landing craft nears the beach, to calm their nerves. Then it occurred to me that the very absence of recipes or references to gardens gives the whole episode a bleakness, a sort of inhuman quality which is really very suitable for the ugly theme of the passage.'

'Yes. In fact – think about it – how about making that a policy from now on? The basic greyness and grottiness of Richard's destiny underscored by lack of any refer-ence to the good and gentle things of life, like food and gardening?'

Kipling fell in with this idea eagerly. Thus by now, important artistic decisions could be taken on the wing as it were. The contrast with the struggles of the earlier days, with the slow evolution of the 'Snapshot' technique, or the uncertainty over the roles of Rex and Prince, was now very marked and the way ahead was beginning to look smooth and clear.

The Beginning of the End

'I have in mind,' said Kipling, 'to write a major scene in which all the important characters in Paul's story offer their comments on, as it were, his progress so far. A sort of review, set on or about his eighteenth birthday, in which people such as Alf, Elsie and Uncle Ted, and perhaps the Brooks, comment on his metamorphosis from an inarticulate, raw young pit-village brat into the Oxford scholar and promising young artist of 1960. I'm not sure, though how to present it.'

Johnson thought for a while. 'A sort of "This is Your Life", you mean? But Paul's a bit, well, obscure to be on "This is your Life" isn't he? Wait a bit – what if he became an overnight celebrity, by e.g. marrying Princess Margaret. Was she available in 1960? We could look it up.'

'I can think of at least two grave difficulties in the way of that idea. First, everybody knows that Princess Margaret in actual fact married Lord Whatsisname, I suppose Paul could simply have his name romantically, as they say, linked with the Princess but even that would raise the second difficulty, which is that I would have to write dialogue, at least a little, for Princess Margaret and so render myself open to charges of libel or treason or something of the kind.'

'Not if Paul just wrote letters to her. Letters that were never sent, like with Ailsa?'

'But if they were never sent, how could Paul become a celebrity and so be interviewed on "This is Your Life"?'

'How about if they were poems? A slim volume of verse, dedicated and/or addressed to Princess Margaret. Published. Overnight fame. No, wait a bit, it's no good.

If they did a "This is Your Life" on Paul on that basis, obviously Princess Margaret would have to swan in at some point and what could she say? "Hello Eamonn, I have never seen this Kane character before in my life and so have zero to contribute at this point in time. Goodbye". Also, I don't suppose she would have come, anyway.'

'Obviously,' said Kipling. 'It must be something much more realistic. And modest. I had thought that perhaps Paul could invite everybody round to a reading of his poems. Then as he read them, people could mentally review, and wonder at, and so on, his transformation . . .'

'Alf, Elsie, Richard, Rex and Prince, Uncle Ted, the Brooks, all sitting around in 12 Alma Terrace, attentively, while Paul reads his poems out? Really?' Johnson raised his eyebrows.

'No, it won't quite do,' Kipling agreed reluctantly. 'Could we make it Speech Day do you suppose? Paul would go up for various scholastic prizes, while people mentally review and so on. The dogs could not be there, of course, but they would have little to contribute in any case and everyone else could very plausibly be present.'

'Possible. But there's nothing to eat at Speech Day. So how would we get recipes in? They could all chew gum-drops or something I suppose, but who wants gum-drop recipes? What if Paul was terribly ill and everybody sits round his bed, having flashbacks and reviewing his progress? If we made him terribly ill with food poisoning that would allow for one or more recipes very naturally. Also insecticide on vegetables might be involved in the food poisoning so we could do some gardening tips ref. pesticides and their dangers, as well.'

'That would do, I suppose. Though it would rather be allowing the recipes and gardening matters to call the tune as it were, when I did intend to keep them as incidentals or grace-notes.'

'Perhaps Uncle Ted, stricken by grief, could go sort of berserk and madly reel off dozens of recipes and gardening stuff at Paul's bedside. Like a bit of James Joyce sort of thing. Then we could be shut of recipes and gardening tips for good. If Uncle Ted gives about a dozen of each, at one fell swoop, what reader could reasonably demand more?'

'Elsie would be more likely than Ted to behave in that way, I think. But it could fatally unbalance the scene and take the emphasis away from Paul. This is turning out rather tricky, I fear.'

Kipling fell silent. I made them some tea.

'Anyway how many words is it so far?' asked Johnson suddenly.

'About fifty thousand words, I think. Why do you ask?'

'Well, you had best be thinking of how its going to end, sort of setting up an ending–type run-in situation, I think, you know.'

'Why, for heaven's sake?' Kipling was evidently appalled. 'The meat of the book is yet to come. The university years, the breakthrough as a poet, the editorship of Isis, meeting interesting people instead of all these ghastly miners and grammar school boys and dogs and provincial lefties – I had thought of at least another sixty to seventy thousand words.'

'Well, suit yourself. But I've been talking round the place a bit and my publishing contacts such as they are, are pretty clear that unless you are famous already novel-wise they will only look at short things that can go straight into paperback. Like about sixty thousand words. More than sixty thousand, and it takes too much glue to stick them together or something.'

'Glue! The bounds of literary inspiration are now set by glue!'

'Well, maybe not glue. Maybe the SOGAT people can't count past sixty thousand or something, but I've been checking around and its true. New books are either very fat, like a half-million words and are about aeroplane disasters or the Devil and things or pocket-size and about something else. Sorry to hit you with this.

I thought you knew.'

'I could start again, I suppose. Yes, I could start again.' Kipling took off his glasses and rubbed the bridge of his nose wearily.

'Not necessary. What about a sequel?' said Johnson casually as if he had said 'What about another cup of tea?' 'End this one as he leaves school or something, then write a follow-up about Oxford etc. *Paul Kane Revisited* sort of thing.'

This was arguably one of the more important moments in the history of the post-war English novel. In one second of casual inspiration, Johnson had both quite possibly saved *Grey Journey* from the dustbin and simultaneously sown the seed of the idea of the trilogy. *Tent Pegs* and *Quiet Tiger* were conceived in that moment, Paul Kane in that moment began his ascent from being just another fictional working-class boy made good (albeit a brilliantly realized one) to being, in the words of the *Sunday Times* reviewer, 'The symbol of a generation, of a time, of a place. There is something of all of us in Paul Kane, and something of Paul Kane in all of us.'

All that Kipling said, however, was 'What a good idea.' He replaced his glasses, firmly. 'That,' he said, 'is what we will do. I think I've also got an idea for the major scene we were talking of a moment ago.' He went on. 'What about a school play? Paul in the lead, or in a major part, anyway. Parents and so on, in the audience, naturally linking their perception of Paul's growth to maturity with their reactions to the play.'

'Brilliant. But what about food and gardening?'

'I think I have an idea for that as well. Let me rough it out and see what you think.' The roughed out version has fortunately survived.

'Oh, that this too, too, solid flesh would melt.' Paul Kane's clear young voice rang out over the packed school hall. The traditional simple all-black dress of Hamlet threw the rather angular lines of his face into bold relief, heightened by the primitive spotlight. He was alone on the stage, yet somehow his slight figure seemed to fill it.

'He looks a right pillock,' thought Richard Kane. Richard was unwillingly wearing his good charcoal-grey suit with an eggshell blue shirt, blue tie and well polished black shoes. The collar chafed. He did not want to be there, sitting on a hard wooden folding chair sullenly chewing a Rowntrees Clear Gum and watching his little brother play Hamlet. He was there to please his mother. 'Solid flesh be buggered,' he thought, "E were never two pennorth o' nowt, for weight nor muscle. T'were 'ardly a pleasure to belt 'im. And yet, sitheee, 'e'll surpass me, for all my rippling physical power that strains at the seams o' this 'ere charcoal-grey best suit. Brass, women all 'e wants, 'e'll 'ave, by t'use o' them brains of his and t'use of a cosy social system aptly symbolized t'other day by t'election o' Macmillan to be Chancellor o' t'University of Oxford, of which Paul will very shortly be an undergraduate member, sithee. Me for t'pit for t'rest o' my days. Paul for t'world o' Macmillan and his mates at Oxford. That's where solid bloody flesh gets thee!'

'Fie on't! O, fie, 'tis an unweeded garden that grows to seed.'

Paul's controlled passion held the audience in total silence. Mr Brook was sitting in the fifth row, wearing a dark grey suit, white shirt and grey tie. Mr Brook's thoughts flew back, as he heard the phrase "unweeded garden" to his first meeting with Paul Kane, and to the *contretemps* of his uncalled-for advice on the moving of larger shrubs to a boy whose home lacked an indoor lavatory let alone a garden. Four years. Four years in which he had learned from Paul Kane, miner's son, how to refine his analysis of English urban society in the mid-twentieth century, learned to adjust his primitive Marxist model of labour relationships, to take account of the fact that as Paul had remarked on the depressing morning

149

after the 1959 election 'the State itself is now the major employer of labour at all levels so that the rhetoric of master and man is now totally inappropriate and you ought perhaps to re-examine your attachment to such rhetoric'. Four years in which this child of the slums had helped him to widen his horizons on foreign affairs. That very month, Paul had politely stopped him in full flow on the phenomenon of Yugoslav 'liberal' Communism, accused him of undue Euro-centricity and warned him to be on the alert for a dramatic swing towards dictatorship in Indonesia (Paul's prophecy was fulfilled within days as Sukarno dissolved the Indonesian Parliament). Four years in which Brook senior had learned many things from Paul, but above all, humility.

'What do you think of it so far?' asked Kipling.

'Brilliant. Really. But aren't they all going to sound a bit alike, Alf and Elsie and everybody? I say, what about having those grotty kids back, those who passed for the grammar school when Paul did. They could all be in *Hamlet*, in bit parts and you could show how they all progressed a bit, but not as much as Paul. You could have ghastly Roger Knowles, the grocer's kid, as Claudius. Then Paul could get to kill him, not before time if you ask me. Anyway, if you have it all happen in a lively bit of the play like the fencing bit at the end where they all get killed, you could have ready-made action courtesy of the Bard himself. They could get the girls from the girls' grammar school over to play Ophelia etc. Stephen Brook could be Horatio.'

'That is an excellent inspiration! Action, character, visual colour – all hinged around the mental action of the players within the action of the play!'

'Might work,' said Johnson modestly, and Kipling set to work vigorously on the first draft.

Journey's End

'Give them the foils, young Osric – Cousin Hamlet,

150

you know the wager?'

Roger Knowles was brilliantly cast as Claudius. Already at eighteen balding a little and running to fat, his body hinted at a mixture of self-indulgence and slyness uneasily co-habiting with powerful greed and lusts. His stage crown of gold-painted cardboard, very convincing from the other side of the footlights, from close by made an odd match in its indeterminate tawdriness for his expressionless, cold, light-brown eyes. His royal cloak was of a rich shimmering dark green. He handled it well on stage. He handled it well now:

'Give them the foils, young Osric.'

The cloak matched the silkiness of his voice. He held it tightly about him, and its rippling greenness gave his thick body an oddly reptilian quality, like that of a puff-adder.

'You know the wager?'

His pale brown eyes held Paul's. For many a long year he had known the wager, though not a word of it had he ever spoken to Paul Kane. Could the grocer's boy outdo the miner's lad? There was the wager. Could relative affluence, a bit of careful cheating now and then, the odd nod and wink from Roger's father to his well-placed friends; the shiny satchel and the talent for sycophancy; the new blazer and the eye for the main chance: could all this outdo what Paul Kane had – sublime, innocent intelligence? Six appropriate 'O' levels each. Three good 'A' levels each. Through the last years at grammar school the contestants were evenly locked, like two well-matched stags, the combat nonetheless savage for the fact that one of the combatants, Paul Kane, was quite unaware that he was in a battle at all. Learning, to Paul, was no battle but a simple joy, like swigging fizzy pop. Gulp it down, wipe your mouth with the back of your hand, feel the sting of the bubbles, laugh for sheer pleasure.

Paul's lack of awareness was amply compensated by

Roger Knowles' spider-like concentration on the struggle, on the marks, on the best way to get an 'A' from old Smith or young Jones, the best way to guess the test questions, to lay out the plans, to pass the exams. Roger and his father read Paul Kane's 'O' and 'A' level results more avidly than Roger's own, poring over the local newspaper under the pinched light of a forty watt bulb, trying to extract some message from the bare announcement of passes and grades, some clue as to where the advantage lay. The threat from Bailey, Bannister, Martin, Brain Owen and all the rest of the Mexthorpe 'workhouse brats' had fallen away, over the years. Only Kane remained, aspiring to University education, aspiring, unbearably, to equal or outdo the grocer's son, to equal or outdo the respectable boy, the boy with clean socks and shiny new shoes. As Hamlet to Claudius, so was Paul Kane – by his mere existence a living rebuke and slight to Roger Knowles.

And now the contest was over. Paul Kane on this evening of 21 March, 1960 was an Exhibitioner of Cornwall College, Oxford. Roger Knowles had tried. Tried Oxford, tried Cambridge, London, Manchester. Everywhere, the same story. Not this year. Not quite. Sorry.

'Dear Mr Knowles,

We are sorry that at the moment we cannot . . .'
Roger Knowles was like some figure in an Edgar Allan Poe story, his options closing in on him like the walls of a nightmare room. He thought, desperately, of Sandhurst. That would at least save him from the scald of direct comparison with Kane. But Sandhurst was 'sorry, but at the moment . . .' So on that sharp March evening Prince Hamlet, Exhibitioner of Cornwall College, Oxford, all unknowingly faced a Claudius sick with real resentment, with real if tangled feelings of rage and worthlessness, a Claudius who that very morning had finally had news of a mocking 'success', more bitter than outright failure.

152

He had been accepted to read for a degree in History at the University of Nottingham.

'Brilliant,' said Johnson, 'what a terrific portrait of Knowles. And what a good job you never followed up my short-sighted idea of having Knowles eaten by dogs when the Kanes went to Scarborough. Don't you think "puff-adder" a bit strong, though? He's still only a kid after all even though a repellent one.'

'Yes. My problem was to find a simile of something reptilian, shimmering yet rather fat, and also menacing. I thought initially of toads, but they are not very menacing, I think.'

'Also they are not reptiles. "Knowles had an oddly amphibian quality" would sound wrong. Tricky. What about grass-snakes? They're green and fairly nasty, but not as nasty as puff-adders.' Johnson paused. 'I don't know. Hey, how about making him a worm? You do see some fat worms, and it would sort of cut the little git down to size, just being a worm not a snake or anything.'

'In that case his cloak would have to be pink, if he is to be a worm. I suppose it could be pink? I'll leave this one for now if you don't mind, because I really would value your opinion about the end of the passage, where Knowles or Knowles/Claudius as it were, is destined for Nottingham.'

'Well, I did wonder about annoying people with that. Why not just send him to unspecified Redbrick?'

'I reasoned that to damn Knowles/Claudius as it were to Redbrick in general could offend a large number of readers, namely all Redbrick graduates and dons. To send him to one fairly small named Redbrick, though, could only offend a relative handful of readers.'

'Fair enough. Good thinking in fact. What next?'

'I thought we could use the wretched Brian Owen, the boy who was beaten up by his atrocious family on the day of the eleven-plus results, his letter from the local education authority you recall, being used as a handkerchief by his father. He could have spent his grammar school years in distant admiration tinged with slight envy of Paul. He could be destined for a management traineeship in a department store or some wretched equivalent and the pathos of both his past life and his future fate could be symbolized by casting him as Polonius or possibly as Rosencrantz, dispatched to his pointless death without ever understanding what is going on.'

'Great. Also he would have to leave his glasses off to play any part at all, *natürlich*, so he could see the whole drama through a sort of uncomprehending fog with the giant figure of Paul/Hamlet sort of looming dimly and then stabbing him for who knows what weird reason.'

'Excellent idea. Then I thought we could use Freda Mitchell as Gertrude.'

'Good stuff. Just one thing, what about order? I mean, we've just had Hamlet and Claudius in the fencing bit at the end, but Polonius and Rosencrantz and people are all dead by then, I think.'

'Yes, you are right. It would be much better not to dart about within the play but to have all the action concentrated in one scene, and preferably the final fencing scene, since there is so much action there. Is there anyone still alive by that time who could be a futile, doomed figure for Brian Owen to play?'

Together Kipling and Johnson examined the text of Act 5 of Hamlet and decided that the banal nonentity Osric was a suitable part for Owen.

Kipling was now ready to write. Magnificently ready.

'This is too heavy, let me see another.' Clive Brown, playing Laertes, tested the balance of the foil with the genuine expertise of a boy with good 'A' levels in Maths and Physics, and then moved away from centre-stage.

'This likes me well. These foils have all a length?' queried Paul/Hamlet lightly.

'Ay, my good lord,' replied Osric. 'Ay, my good

lord,' thought Brian Owen, wearily, sweating under the thick black wig he wore as Osric. 'How the hell would I know how long they are? I can't even see the bloody things. Yet what could I not have achieved, had my siblings not persisted in breaking my glasses, tearing up or actually eating my exercise books and essential texts, defecating in the wretched carrier bags which served me as satchels, and in countless other ways both overt and subtle demonstrated a gross lack of support for my academic efforts, sithee?'

Laertes and Hamlet fenced. Hamlet claimed a hit.

'A hit, a very palpable hit!' cried Osric enthusiastically.

'Always a hit, that Paul Kane,' mused Brian Owen. 'Winning prizes. Going to Oxford. Doing English, History, all the things I'd have liked to do. I was forced to specialize in bloody Maths, it being the only subject you can if necessary do in your head, without benefit of books or even of glasses, come to that.'

Hamlet and Laertes fenced on with increasing passion. Osric was asked again for a judgement.

'Nothing, either way,' cried Osric.

'That's about it,' thought Brian Owen. 'It matters nowt either way. Maths, English, so what? They've fixed me up a management traineeship at bloody Marks and Spencers. In a sense, perhaps, its through Paul Kane that the rest of my life must be lived since a combination of wretched circumstances and my own feebleness of character prevent me living for myself, as it were, sithee. Paul Kane must live for me, aye and for all the rest of us wretches, Osrics and Guildensterns to his Hamlet, left behind in Mexthorpe as he meteors off to Oxford.'

The foils flashed, the deadly mock fight of Hamlet and Laertes swayed to and fro across the stage. A brief pause. Time now for Gertrude to drink the poisoned wine.

'He's fat and scant of breath.

Here Hamlet, take my napkin, rub thy brows.

The queen carouses to thy fortune, Hamlet,' cried Freda Mitchell. 'Fat, indeed,' she thought to herself. 'He's got a figure like a young god. But, like a god, he notices not me. He passes me by, as indeed does everything else. What avails the talent for languages which has secured me good 'A' levels in French and German, when the relative prosperity which has characterized the *soi-disant* Macmillan years has so utterly failed to manifest itself *chez* Mitchell? No *Wirtschaftwunder* for us. Here I stand in the robes of a Queen, namely a dark-blue, high waisted full length dress, with ruched bodice and fur trim at wrists and hem, yet since morning I've only had one digestive biscuit and a little Tizer and this evening I shall return to more hours of toil helping my mother make rugs. And yet, it would all be worth it, just for one glance from Paul Kane! One glance!'

The queen died on the steps of the throne.

'Look to the queen there, ho!' cried Brian Owen/ Osric in his final, characteristically futile contribution to the drama.

'Ay, some bugger look to the queen,' he cried inwardly. 'For without my glasses I surely can't!'

The tragedy came to its dying fall.

'Go bid the soldiers shoot,' ordered Fortinbras. So the tragedy ended. The curtain fell. Curtain-calls, with Paul Kane shyly triumphant, at the centre. Final fall of the curtain. Babble. 'Well done, people!' 'I thought I'd fluffed that line when . . .' 'You were great!' 'Well done!' 'Terry had a bloody great hole in his tights . . .' 'Fencing looked really good . . .'

Slowly people became aware that Freda Mitchell was still lying where she had fallen, near the throne.

'Come on, Freda!' 'Stop messing about!' ejaculated various cast-members.

'Be quiet!' commanded Paul, bending swiftly to take her pulse. 'Shift that throne out of the way, I'm taking her to the Head's study.' He picked her up easily. 'Somebody go and get that big fruit cake and a quantity of milk, from the changing room. Bring them to the Head's study.' His manner brought instant obedience.

In the Head's study, he set Freda down in a deep dark green, stud-backed leather armchair. She stirred.

'Take it easy, Freda,' murmured Paul. People crowded into the study, Alf and Elsie, Uncle Ted and Richard, the Brooks, Roger Knowles, Brian Owen and the rest of the cast, Mr Sylvester the drama teacher, Mr Binney, the Head and other staff members.

'What is the matter with her?' quavered the Headmaster.

'Hunger, sir. Just hunger,' opined Paul authoritatively. 'Pass me a slice of the fruit cake and a glass of milk, Steve. Now then.' he turned gently to Freda. 'Just try to eat a bit of this. Have some milk to help it down. It contains 10oz castor sugar, for instantly available energy, also 10oz butter, 5 protein-packed eggs, 12oz flour, 3oz ground almonds, and lots of nutritional, vitamin-rich fruit, i.e. ¼lb raisins, ¼ glacé cherries, ¼ sultanas. Here, try this bit of glacé cherry. The actual fruit can be varied according to taste you know,' murmured Paul. 'Just make sure you bake for 2½ hours at oven Mark 4.' The room was silent, Freda ate a small piece of cake slowly. Uncle Ted found himself noticing the pot of African violets on the headmaster's desk. They were surprisingly healthy, considering their notorious choosiness in the matter of watering and their propensity to react badly to temperature changes. 'I'd choose bulbs, myself for an office,' thought Ted. 'Never African violet. But then I'd not a looked for t'likes of our Paul to thrive so mightily in a pit village. So it just shows. Tha' never knows, nor can tell, for certain sure, sithee na' then.'

Paul Kane fed Freda little pieces of fruit cake, like one feeding a shy, small bird. Around him, parents, teachers, friends and enemies surrounded him, each one seeing him in their different way, each one mulling and turning their memories of this boy dressed as Hamlet, now reminding the sensitive among them irresistibly of St Francis. Outside the study, the crowds dispersed from the hall, into the frosty night air. Mr Templeton, the school caretaker, went to turn the heat off. The town stretched greyly around the school and poked one finger of stone and slate up the valley towards Mexthorpe. The hills held them all, school, town, Mexthorpe, pits and people in a firm embrace. At 12 Alma Terrace Rex stirred in his sleep, Prince sighed. The hard Yorkshire stars looked down.

In Washington, USA, it was still only four in the afternoon. A man called Kennedy was preparing for another long evening of running for President. It was 21 March. The first spring of the 1960s was a few hours old.

I had never seen Johnson so moved. He made a great show of blowing his nose and pretending to have something in his eye, before he spoke.

'Well, that's it. Magnificent.'

'Thank you. But aren't there any little points? You've such a tremendous eye for detail,' replied Kipling.

'Just one thing – but its so piffling –'

'Please.'

'Oh, well. It's just that I figure there are upwards of fifty people in the Head's study for the final scene, so its a bit, well, crowded.'

'A good point. I will have a look at that. Now, next, I thought we would have Paul go home, then a few months later he could get on the train for Oxford and his family could see him off, as it were.'

'Next!' said Johnson. 'How can there be a *next* after a scene like that? That's the end. Finito. You can't improve on that. It's the end. If they want any more, they'll have to read the sequel.'

'Do you really think so? I had thought . . . But I

suppose that scene does, come to think, have a certain quality of finality, actually. All right. Agreed. End. So what do we do now? It feels rather odd, doesn't it?'

There was a tangible sense of loss in the air, as it suddenly struck all of us that this great and various band of pilgrims, Paul Kane, Kipling, Elsie, Alf, Johnson, Uncle Ted and all the rest had, for the moment at least, completed their pilgrimage and must now go their separate ways.

'What's the title going to be?' asked Johnson.

'I had thought *Golden Voyage*, tentatively,' said Kipling.

'Nice. I like the journey theme idea, but *Golden Voyage* sounds a bit upbeat. There's a lot of sadness and heartache etc. in it. What about *Black Journey*?'

'That sounds rather grim. Paul does win through in the end, after all.'

'Though a lot of his friends don't – they have to go to Nottingham or work in Marks and Spencers and things.'

'And yet,' countered Kipling, 'even during the journey as it were, there is much simple pleasure for Paul, and others, such as the day at the canal with Uncle Ted.'

'Would a compromise be in order?' I ventured. 'What about *Grey Journey*?' So it was, as the world knows, finally decided. Johnson pointed out that a true compromise between 'Golden' and 'Black' would be some sort of brown or khaki but quickly agreed that *Khaki Journey* would, as a title, be very misleading and *Brown Journey* would sound somehow contrived.

The Lost Chapters

I believe that this plain account will dispose of the malicious canard that Johnson 'ghosted' the Paul Kane trilogy for Kipling and also of the less malicious but still quite incorrect idea that the Paul Kane novels were in any sense the product of two authors, that Kipling and Johnson were the brothers Goncourt of our time, so to speak.

Johnson himself always strenuously refused any printed public acknowledgement of his assistance in the form of dedications, prefaces or the like and I hope that my account has shown that this was no false modesty on his part. As a catalyst, as an inspiration at difficult moments and as a second pair of eyes on the look-out for inconsistencies of plot and so on he was invaluable, and in the early days, indispensable. But, as he himself always vigorously insisted, the glory, the pain, the responsibility for the creation of Paul Kane and his world belong to Peter Kipling alone.

A full understanding of the mind of Peter Kipling, the artist, and of his working relationship with Johnson is, I believe, not possible without reference to a fact which I now make public for the first time. Several chapters of *Grey Journey* amounting to some twenty thousand words in all, were written by Kipling, with Johnson's help, in addition to the text of the published version. It is to the nature and content of these 'Lost Chapters', and to the circumstances which led to their composition and to their eventual non-publication, that we must now turn.

The Lost Chapters. A Fresh Start

Kipling was irritated when the first publisher he approached returned his manuscript with many favourable comments but also with the opinion that the novel was too short, and stood in need of a further twenty thousand words to suit, as they put it, their 'list'. He was mortified beyond measure when two more publishing houses repeated the substance of this advice.

Naturally, he felt resentment towards Johnson, who had so confidently advised him to stop work at sixty thousand words.

'But I'm right, dammit!' said Johnson, 'Who's telling you eighty thousand? Some dozy little girl with a two-two in English Literature from Exeter, what does she know?'

160

'Well, what do you know?' retorted Kipling. 'You work in a bank, after all's said and done, you're not an author. But you know all about recipes and Whoever Sanctions and sixty thousand words – how? Why should I believe you?'

'It works, doesn't it? All these publishing prats have said is "give us more of it", right? And what did they say to that other thing of yours you told me about, that story *Love Has Sensitive Teeth*, what about that?'.

'At that time' said Kipling stiffly, 'I was, on advice, writing about subjects with which I was closely familiar. I was having a lot of dental work done at that period and in any case that is a long time ago.'

'Right!' cried Johnson. 'Before you met me. Now look at you. Sixty thousand words of good stuff and not a word of it about dental amalgam, not a water-drill in sight!'

'Don't go on so about *Sensitive Teeth*. It was an ill-planned story, ill-advised, I agree. But it was a long time ago –'

'And it stank! It was the world's ninth worst story, the other eight being in Walloon –'

'So now I have sixty thousand words, according to you, in the Hardy-Lawrence league, and nobody wants it. Wonderful!'

'Yes they do, you dummy. They want more. Extra. Additional.' There was a long silence. Kipling walked to the window which looked out across the garden towards the parish church.

'How can I make it longer?' he asked finally, in a low voice.

'First,' said Johnson, 'I think we should have some tea.'

They drank the tea in an awkward silence. Johnson finally spoke, hesitantly.

'What if we had a little shift of literary gear, towards the thriller for instance?'

'*The Whoever Sanction*? Certainly not. No.'

'No, no, we stick with Paul Kane and send him to

161

Oxford but fill up twenty thousand words with one of those Oxbridge-based detective-type things, you know, jokes in Greek, lots of sherry, not much sex, bodies in quads. We could weave it all in coherence-wise by making Paul alone able to solve the murder when nobody else can, actually just because he's working-class and everything. Say, the Provost or Dean or somebody gets murdered. And nobody knows who did it.'

'What a novel twist,' said Kipling curtly. 'Nobody knows who did it! We could have discovered a whole new genre here. We might call it "the whodunit" perhaps.'

'All right. Very funny. Just listen. Say he gets murdered, i.e. the Provost with a strange object, and nobody knows what it is except Paul. He knows what it is only too grimly well. It's a Tizer bottle.'

'That would not take me twenty thousand words to express, I think.'

'There would be lots of other stuff. Mysterious footprints in the shrubbery made by clogs so *natürlich* these Oxford pansies don't know what they are. And a small quantity of tripe or black pudding, clutched in the dead man's hand, fibres from a pair of braces, a ferret howling in the night, all meaningless until Paul's deep and hardwon background knowledge of ferrets and things make it all click into place. Now, here's the beauty of it – all this only takes up Paul's first couple of weeks at Oxford, so when this book, *Grey Journey* ends, Rebecca, Elaine and the hurtling gargoyles are all still safely in the future, in the nice, meaty sequel.

'I think I would like a cup of tea.'

'OK. Rethink,' said Johnson. 'He could fall asleep on the train, on the way to Oxford, and dream for twenty thousand words.'

'What would he dream about?'

'Well, his past life would all flash before him.'

'I have already written about his past life. At length. In detail,' retorted Kipling, in a tone of some asperity.

I made them some more tea.

'What if,' Johnson persisted, 'he gets cold feet ref. Oxford. What if in like July 1960 he suddenly thinks he doesn't want to go to Oxford, or he's scared of it deep down etc., but he doesn't want to just go down the pit with his dad or work at Marks and Spencers like thingy. He wants a free, open air life, working-class and definitely manual but somehow the exact opposite of being a miner.'

'You mean he aspires to become a steeplejack?' queried Kipling coolly.

'Something like that. Just for twenty thousand words, i.e. a couple of months, then, of course, he sees the light and goes to Oxford after all. What about a spell on a farm?'

'A farm? It would bring in more characters... I would have to research it,' mused Kipling. 'I know less of farms than of coalmines, actually. And yet... Paul's progress is arguably a little bland, from the point of view of self-doubt, as things have gone so far. I will give it some thought. Thank you.'

I could almost see Kipling's creative fires slowly re-kindling at last.

The necessary research was lengthy and it was several weeks before Kipling was able to sketch out the following passage, which I here reproduce at some length, both because of its intrinsic quality and its high interest to the student of literature.

On August 8th 1960 the United Nations demanded the withdrawal of Belgian troops from the Congo. Dag Hammarskjöld stood poised to enter what would be for him and for thousands of humbler people the fatal amphitheatre of Katanga. On that pregnant day Paul Kane was emphatically not reading in preparation for his undergraduate career.

He was instead walking down a long track, rough with white limestone chippings, high on the Wolds of East Yorkshire. He was wearing a thick grey collarless flannel shirt, brown corduroy trousers and thick-soled, very scuffed brown boots. He carried only a khaki ex-army haversack. The track led from the main road, between huge fields of harvest-ready high-grade malting barley towards Home Farm, where Paul Kane was seeking work as a farm labourer.

He approached the farm house cautiously, alert for over-zealous dogs, noting the typical Yorkshire Wolds farm layout of ash and poplar windbreak sheltering a large pond, home to a tribe of Khaki Campbell ducks and sheltering likewise a large cobbled stack-yard, a strongly nucleated group of five to seven brick outbuildings, and the farm house itself with its roof-pitch and style of windows clearly distinctive of the eighteen-eighties. Before he could knock on the green-painted front door, it was opened by a tall, sandy-haired man of fifty or so with a broad, freckled face, wearing a grey cotton jacket, crumpled grey trousers, and well polished black shoes.

'Mr Thorpe?' queried Paul, politely.

'Aye,' said the man guardedly.

'Mrs Hargreaves at the pub mentioned your name. I'm looking for harvest work possibly with a view to a permanent position and she said you might be taking on.'

'You're not from round here,' observed the farmer Thorpe, accurately.

'No, indeed,' agreed Paul. 'You have no doubt discerned that the shortness of my vowel sounds, as in the word "your" for instance or "might", mark me out as a native of Yorkshire indeed, but of the industrial south of the county. A true Easterner would have produced sounds more like "yooer" or "maight", illustrating the links of the local accent with North Lincolnshire.'

'Aye,' rejoined Thorpe shrewdly, 'and I'll bet, despite the educated verbal overlay, no doubt a product of a grammar school education, you're not yourself above the occasional use of a 'sithee' – or 'sither', so very characteristic of South Yorkshire, whereas you would never insert a 'v' between terminal and opening vowels as we do locally in an expression like 'used to v'it'. But' – he changed the subject disconcertingly sharply, 'What's your knowledge o' farm work coming as you avowedly do from an area characterized by heavy industry, coal-mining and a fundamentally urban culture?'

'Not much, but I'm strong and willing, and I'm learning,' rejoined Paul stoutly. 'I know that the Yorkshire Wolds are basically a Jurassic-Oolithic limestone ridge, intruded into a Cretaceous chalk tableland, and consequently well drained, light in soil but fertile. High grade malting barley, wheat and oats thrive and sheep are also of some local importance. Large holdings are the rule, farms of four hundred acres being not uncommon, and large fields of 20 acres or so are likewise the norm. These two factors are helping to lead to rapid mechanization, especially of the harvesting processes.'

'What of sugar beet and t'other root-crops?' Thorpe queried sharply.

'Again, of local importance,' rejoined Paul, 'but slightly on the decrease as mechanization and subsidies make crops such as malting barley increasingly attractive.'

'I took you for an ignorant townee, youth. Seems I mistook,' said Farmer Thorpe in admiration. 'But what brings an educated-sounding young fellow like you to my door seeking work at stooking and swich?'

'Fundamentally,' said Paul, 'a doubt about whether I can honestly continue my education, and its concomitant inevitable distancing of my personality from my social roots, in a spirit of true moral seriousness. I foresee that the year 1960 will mark the end of the relatively austere earnestness of the 'fifties and wartime period, and the start of a period of hedonism, conspicuous consumption and fashionable political cynicism, in which idealism will be at a discount.'

Thorpe eyed Paul sharply. 'What of Senator Kennedy?' he queried. 'Will not his election, if it takes place, mark a commitment to youthful idealism at least on the part of the American electorate?'

'Only superficially, I fear,' Paul shook his head, sadly. 'The Kennedy régime, granted his success in November, in retrospect, I am sure, will be seen as a manipulative sham, a thing of rhetoric and style, not substance. And in this coming epoch of cynicism and opportunism which Senator Kennedy may indeed come to symbolize, I fear it will be too hard for me to keep as it were my moral feet at the University of Oxford. The temptation to use my time to acquire a hard veneer of sophistication, to gain useful *entrées* and to make influential friends, the urge to use the final degree as a passport to some exploitative career in journalism, public relations or even as a right-wing Labour MP, these temptations I feel I could not confidently resist. Why, you are no doubt wondering, do I not therefore stay at home, take a teacher-training course, perhaps, or even join my father and brother down the pit? Partly because such gestures would have too emphatic and theatrical an air, partly for less worthy motives, namely that my neighbours will believe that I avoided Oxford out of mere fear of failure. So I came away, in search of some way of living that would be acceptable and yet not fall into the error of moral priggishness (of all my books Pascal's *Pensées* is the only one I have brought with me) – and so I find myself, in the course of that search, here on your doorstep.'

'I appreciate your dilemma, lad,' replied Thorpe, 'and though I think it has overtones of a desire to be morally '*plus royaliste que le roi*' as it were, that's to be forgiven at your age. I'll take you on, until harvest's led, any road. Seven ten a week, less board, plus overtime.'

'Don't keep t'lad on t'doorstep all day, Frank.'

The voice was that of Mrs Thorpe, who, wearing a dark-blue dress with white revers and cuffs and medium height blue court shoes, hustled Paul into the big airy kitchen, and presented him with a huge pot of tea and a gargantuan blue plate, piled high with scones.

Sitting in that bright country kitchen looking out across a homely vegetable garden full of well-watered, correctly spaced lettuce, towards fields of sunlit whitening barley and rippling wheat, Paul's mind yet ran back remorselessly to his dilemma.

'Terrific. What happens next then, for twenty thousand words?' asked Johnson.

'There's the eternal rhythm of the seasons, ploughing, harvest, and er, ploughing again,' Kipling clearly faltered at this point.

'He's only there for two months.'

'So he is. Well, farms are quite lively places. One could have haystacks catching fire, and horses running amok, and a friend of mine was once bitten quite severely by a pig. Perhaps Paul could cut himself on a scythe, I believe that they are awfully dangerous in the hands of the novice. He could bear a permanent scar to remind him forever of the rural experience,' suggested Kipling.

'Yes. Great! Galloping through the blazing rickyard, fighting off crazed pigs with a scythe – it could be incredibly visual, especially if we shot it at night. My God we could reconstruct the whole thing around this. Totally scrub *Grey Journey* call it *The Pigs*. These pigs get rabies, you see and eat people and threaten the whole village. Sod the village, they could threaten the world, via Sheffield! They all charge off to Sheffield station thousands of them all foaming at the mouth where Paul is just getting on the train to go to Oxford, so he doesn't have to go to the farm at all, the farm comes to him, see? So he's besieged by pigs in this railway carriage, with a lovely girl, *natürlich*, a grovelling coward played by e.g. Dustin Hoffman, Shelley Winters playing somebody, and a quiet old geezer played by Olivier who turns out to be the world expert on rabid pigs and he's an alcoholic and his hands shake, so he can't make up the secret formula – so Paul has to make up a different formula.'

'I think that sort of thing can only obscure the central issues of Paul's emotional and moral development. What I had in mind was, perhaps a very small haystack fire, a slight cut from a scythe and perhaps a little disquiet caused by a skittish horse.'

'OK. A small fire, a slight cut, a very small runaway horse. Now it sounds like *Paul of Sunnybrook Farm*, but suit yourself.'

'I think the best plan would be for me to get Paul settled in and working and see how matters develop,' said Kipling firmly.

Thus it was decided.

Early next morning Thorpe set Paul to work.

'Stook t'Seventeen Acre, lad. Follow the old-fashioned but effective McCormick tractor-drawn reaper-binder round the field, pick up the barley sheaves or "shabs" as we call them locally and arrange them in little houses called "stooks" to dry out thoroughly prior to the process of collecting up the sheaves in carts and bringing them to the stackyard to be stacked in stacks, a process known locally as "leading-in". And with that, Thorpe strolled off.

Paul set to with a will and stooked all day under the August sun. By evening, his hands were chafed and his muscles ached, but he was content.

'It's a bit sort of eerie, don't you think. I mean there seems to be nobody else there. Is he stooking solo? And what about the tractor-driver? Why doesn't he say anything, not even "Hello"?'

'Of course,' sighed Kipling. 'A Freudian slip. I had not been entirely looking forward to creating the necessary gallery of country characters exchanging half-witted rustic dialogue, so I suppose I unconsciously quite forgot to write in the other farm labourers, Paul's colleagues.'

'Half-witted,' mused Johnson, 'What if they really were? Half-witted I mean, so they don't have any dialogue, they just gibber a bit and smile vacantly. Also, they could all look alike so you could do them in one go and never mention them again. Like this:

Paul was introduced to Alf, Ben, Charlie, Dave and Eric, a bunch of half-wits, all wearing identical, er, smocks and all with identical vacant blue eyes, and silly grins. 'These are my staff, the Brown brothers. You'll get along just fine. Just be sure never to mention sheep!' cried Thorpe heartily and buggered off' sort of thing.'

'It is tempting but I think it might be read as somewhat dismissive of the rural working class and also of the mentally handicapped. I think you may have given me the germ of an idea though.'

A day or so later Kipling showed Johnson the following interesting draft.

'Ah divn't know what tha's rightly on about,' opined Shep. Shep was a tiny man, hardly five feet tall, a skilled farmhand, though, and forthright when he chose to speak which was not often. He dragged his pipe from the pocket of his patched and shiny black jacket and fiddled with matches. He and Paul were sitting, leaning against the gate between Top Field and the Seventeen Acre, taking a short rest from stooking. 'In thy place,' continued Shep, 'Ah'd be off to Oxford and be dammed, see. Get thee an education, youth, and get thee a soft job. Think about t'moral consequences when and if they manifest theirselves, not afore, by gum.'

He tossed away a still smouldering match. The stubble of the Seventeen Acre was as dry as timber and in seconds a thin line of smoke and flame was crackling across the cut straw towards the stooked barley.

'Curses!' ejaculated Shep. 'Lay hod on a sack lad, and beat on yon fire or there'll be hell to pay.'

They beat together at the thin but menacing line of flame as other farmhands ran towards them . . . Smoke stung their eyes.

'You see, Shep,' gasped Paul as flying embers burned face and hands, 'the consequences of the sort of existential approach you were just advocating can be devastating. If we take your tossing away of a match as an analogue of my dilemma à *propos* higher education you see how awaiting the possible consequences of an action can only mean a shorthand for leaving things too late!'

'And yet, youth,' retorted the undismayed Shep through the thickening smoke, 'chances o' yon match setting light to t'stubble were hundreds to one.' He beat furiously at the edge of the flames, driving them back by the sheer vigour of his assult. 'We cannot in any case govern our moral conduct by dubious analogies, like t'Schoolmen o't Middle Ages.' He broke off, coughing and beating at his greasy old cap which had begun to smoulder.

The fire was contained. Little damage was done, except to Shep's dignity, but Paul was no nearer a solution of his problem than before.

'You get the idea?' asked Kipling eagerly, 'by making each farm labourer and each incident illustrate some aspect of Paul's central dilemma, I move the plot along and introduce characters but without having tediously to elaborate them and yet I leave the reader in no doubt that this is a mere interlude in the story, and will end as and when Paul's problem is resolved. I've roughed out this list of possible future incidents –

'Rescue of Cow from Pond – Shep challenges Paul's central idea of a 'spirit of the age' able to significantly influence an individual's moral behaviour. But then – Jack Dilly the Shepherd Explains How He Trained His Dog 'Rob' – Dilly challenges the fundamental idea of moral autonomy and vigorously outlines the case for determinism and the behaviouralist standpoint ... However, the Elevator Breaks Down and the Wheat Stack Has To Be Made By Hand – George Holly forcefully makes the case for acting *as if* moral autonomy was a reality closely echoing Pascal's concept of 'The Wager', and taking the broken elevator as a paradigm of the poverty of mechanistic ethics.

'I'm not sure of all the rest but I imagine the last episode involving Jack Dilly falling off a ladder and breaking his leg, thus giving rise to the climactic discussion of the nature of human responsibility involving all the labourers and also Mr and Mrs Thorpe.'

'Terrific' said Johnson. 'Is that it then?'

'Not really. I think I will still need five or six thousand words more from somewhere.'

'What about sending him to London for a bit?'

'Possible. But tricky. A whole new set of people and circumstances, coming right at the end of the book.'

Johnson thought for a moment.

'What if he just gets on a train at York and goes to London, but he never gets there, well, he comes straight back, and what we write is one of those long-journey things where people go on a long train ride and meet colourful picaresque people, but you don't meet anybody for very long.'

'But surely that sort of literary journey normally involves travelling across Siberia, or down to Argentina? Paul's journey from York to King's Cross would take up only four hours or so, barely time to meet one character properly unless he changed his seat a great deal.'

'Great! He changes his seat a lot because he hasn't paid. Ticketless, he seeks to dodge the Ticket Collector, who symbolizes something and engages all sorts of people in conversation who tell him about their lives in flashbacks so it's more like one of those things on a jumbo jet that's going to crash, only it doesn't.'

'Possible,' said Kipling eagerly. 'It would be even better if Paul's train connections were poor, and he had to change trains frequently at real, named places, giving the whole passage an authentic, English journey sort of air on the model of Priestley or Orwell.'

Kipling wrote a fine opening to Paul Kane's journey to London:

> The day on which the US Senate forbade the use of aid funds for the purchase of Cuban sugar found Paul striding purposefully across the River Ouse towards York railway station. He was barely aware of the swirling summer crowds though more than one female head turned to look at him, bronzed and fit in his open-necked egg-shell blue shirt, navy blue blazer, grey light flannel trousers and black shoes. Paul's head was full of the Minster. The soaring ambition of the Chapter House (1286–1307) the delicacy of the great western towers of 1474, the counterpointing rustic solidity of the twelfth-century piers in the crypt all held messages for Paul, but messages indistinct, unclear on the pressing problem of whether or not to take up the Exhibition at Cornwall College. The Railway Museum in the morning and now the Minster in the afternoon: questions but no answers, not here, not now.
>
> As Paul came out of the gothic chill of the Minster, into the warm sunlight his body rather than his mind decided illogically, without argument but with total conviction, that he must look for his answer far from here. He must go to London. He started to walk briskly down Museum Street towards the station.

'Just a couple of things,' said Johnson. 'Do you really mean Paul was "striding across the Ouse?"'

'By way of the Museum Street Bridge, of course,' explained Kipling.

'Oh. I think you'd better say that. It sounds a bit apocalyptic otherwise. More major points – where did he get all these clothes? Blazers etc? When he was up at Home Farm he was dressed up like Worzel Gummidge with an army haversack. What's happened to that, by the way? And does he have any other luggage and if so where did he get it and where is it now?'

'The bags are at the station,' said Kipling. 'On arrival at York his first act was to buy some decent clothes and suitcase, and rid himself of the haversack. In the river.'

Kipling decided that the actual substance of Paul's railway journey involved such a complex of potential artistic difficulties it would be prudent to prepare the thing in outline and take Johnson's opinion on salient points, before venturing into actual prose.

Paul's journey began on a stopping train from York to Doncaster, and Kipling's plan was ingeniously divided into stages, both of mood and in the literal, physical sense, as the first draft shows clearly:

York to Ricall

Paul's compartment is invaded by a gay crowd of young aristocrats on their way from York races to Doncaster races. They are colourfully dressed in cavalry twill, hacking jackets, cravats etc. (m.) and chiffon dresses (f.). They offer Paul champagne and *pâté* sandwiches. They give him the recipe for the *pâté*. Paul is enchanted by their gaiety and wit (egs. of wit? apposite quotations from Wilde and Sheridan? Shaw etc? or consult joke book?) Paul decides impulsively to go up to Oxford to be among such gay and congenial people.

Ricall to Selby

The scene darkens. Casual but offensive references by young racegoers to coal miners, blacks etc. General insensitivity displayed plus pervasive sense of corruption. Paul symbolically but politely refuses further *pâté* sandwiches and impetuously decides to return to Mexthorpe and become a full-time Labour Party Agent.

Selby to Doncaster

Racegoers become more and more offensive (and drunk). They attempt to throw Paul from train, as a 'joke'. Paul verbally humiliates them, one by one, by dint of superior intelligence and sheer polemical power and integrity. They are penitent. Offer further sandwiches, remorsefully, Paul coolly refuses, but the fact that they are susceptible to remorse causes Paul to defer his hasty decision to return home to Mexthorpe. Decides to go on to London after all, in search of enlightenment as to true nature of English class system and role of social class in determining attitudes. At Doncaster racegoers depart, subdued. Paul changes trains after discussing care of pelargoniums with station porter.

Johnson was enthusiastic about this general outline but had some reservations on detail.

'Why,' he asked, 'would the jolly young aristos not be travelling by Rolls or at least in first class?'

'A good point. As they tumble merrily into the compartment they explain to Paul that they, shall we say, prefer rail travel because one meets such jolly people – this Paul naturally finds disarming – and that the first-class carriages are all full so may they join him?'

'Great. Now about that darkening mood bit – how will you do the pervasive sense of corruption? I can see them being insensitive ref. coal-miners etc., but what's exactly with the corruption?'

'Well I want to convey, that they are all, as it were, corrupt. I need to think this out, obviously.'

'What if it suddenly strikes Paul, between Ricall and Selby that it's the men who are the ones in chiffon dresses and vice versa? And they produce this dead fox out of a hamper and start smearing people with blood etc., and cutting its tail off, laughing hysterically. Then they start sniffing cocaine laughing even more hysterically?'

'How would they have come by a dead fox at York races? Also, they are on their way not to Berlin in the days of Weimar but to Doncaster in 1960. I think your picture, therefore, is extreme.'

'OK. How about this. I think the bit where they try to

sling Paul off the train is dodgy. He would surely have to indulge in karate or something physical, before destroying them verbally, which could be tricky to write, so how about this? One of the young toffs is a half-wit, called Henry. All the other toffs rib him good-naturedly about how he's just lost five grand at the races etc., but quite nicely and so you get your aristocratic coruscating wit like e.g. "When news gets round that Henry's backed a horse people start counting its legs, ha, ha." Then as the mood darkens they start saying rotten things to him, corruptly, like "stop dribbling, Henry, it'll send you blind." So, moved by compassion Paul offers to teach Henry to read. All the young toffs laugh corruptly and throw Henry off the train. Now, steady on, there's no plotting bother with lifeless bodies on the track etc., because by the time they've organized themselves to chuck Henry off the train (they're all pissed remember) while Paul looks on aghast, they've reached Selby station. So they find they've just chucked Henry out on to the station platform to their baffled rage etc. Henry gets back on the train grinning foolishly, Paul then humiliates the corrupt young aristos verbally and, this is really good, he rubs salt in their verbal wounds by, between Selby and Doncaster teaching Henry to read, using *Sporting Life*. What if Henry then refuses to part from Paul, but follows him round like a sort of Caliban? He could mop and mow and things as appropriate and tonelessly screech – "Twenty to one the field" or something at tense moments. It would be very Shakespearean, very epic.'

'Surely the parents of such a severely handicapped young man would never let him go off to the races, carrying thousands of pounds?'

'They would, you know. They don't care about their kids, people like that. But hang on, you're right. They wouldn't give a sod about what happened to Henry but they would give lots of sods about what he did with all that money. So scrub Caliban, scrub Henry. Pity, though, I liked the idea of what you could do with the idea of a sort of Fool-in-King-Lear figure going around with Paul, uttering gnomic utterances. What about a parrot?'

Kipling did not find the idea of a parrot in the least helpful at that particular point, but took up the idea of the young aristocrats illustrating their corruption and callousness by tossing one of their number out of the train onto Selby Station platform and Paul's creative reaction thereto.

Kipling persevered with this technique of planning Paul's journey in broad outline as it was proving so fruitful. The next stage took Paul to Grantham.

Doncaster to East Retford

Two men aged 35 approx., by their charcoal grey two-piece suits, plain white shirts, rolled gold cuff-links and badly chosen ties clearly middle but not professional classes, join Paul. One of the men eats sandwiches but does not offer them round. Silence reigns. Paul reflects that young racegoing aristocrats at least had some generosity of spirit, if erratic (cf. *pâté* sandwiches). Paul reflects further on oppressive mean-spirited dullness of lower middle class.

East Retford to Sutton-on-Trent

The men begin to speak. Unpleasant, semi-educated accents. They exchange hints on more prosaic aspects of gardening e.g. tending runner beans. A recipe for cheese straws is given by one of the men. Paul eagerly offers remarks on care of fuchsias, exquisite delicacy of their blooms. Suggests *profiterolles* as exciting alternative to cheese straws. Is coldly rebuffed. Reflects angrily on mediocre, vulgar philistinism of lower middle class.

Sutton-on-Trent to Newark

Further repellent conversation between the two men. Reveal themselves as racist bigots. Talk animatedly of barbecues, Torremolinos, and, in hostile tones, of Labour Party and women drivers. Paul reflects on stupidity, ignorance and vileness of the lower-middle class.

Newark to Grantham

Two men's conversation yet more animated. Turns to methods of defrauding the Inland Revenue. Men both reveal themselves to be estate agents. Revulsion of Paul. Men murmuring of 'small world', 'fancy that', etc., interrupted by Paul, who excoriates them as philistines, parasites, bigots, corrupt and selfish, worse in their way even than a group of aristocratic corrupt young racegoers who at least have style, humour and fitful generosity. He builds a passionate and massive condemnation of the lower middle class on the failure of the estate agent with sandwiches to pass them round. Men mumble lame apologies. All leave train at Grantham. Men subdued and Paul in mood of grim exaltation. P. decides that whatever the details of his destiny, it lies with the working class or just possibly with the professional classes, but not with the grimy intellectual and moral wasteland which stretches coarsely between the two. Idea of working at Marks and Spencers discarded with finality.

'Terrific', was Johnson's comment. 'Literary-wise, no problems at all, I'd say.'

'Thank you,' said Kipling, 'and for once I really can see the scene as you tend to, in terms of film. I imagine the estate agents as pale, like the sort of grubs you find under stones. Overweight, to the tune of thirty or forty pounds and sweating a good deal. One of them could have one of those little toothbrush moustaches and a copy of the *Daily Mail*. He could have socks that clashed with his tie and glazed, rather fish-like eyes.'

'Great. All good stuff. Just one thing – we've already antagonized all the graduates of Nottingham University and also the management of Marks and Spencers – do we really have to antagonize estate agents? I mean could we say "the men reveal themselves to be estate agents or something of the sort", a bit more sort of vague?'

'Hardly. I believe it would read oddly if the actual

dialogue ran, "What's your line of business then, squire?" "Actually I'm an estate agent or something of the sort." "Well there you go, I'm something of the sort myself." Estate agents they must clearly be, I think.'

For once in their discussions the logic of mundane practicality was on Kipling's side, and Johnson gave way, though with misgivings, I sensed. (The possible reasons for Kipling's particular animus against estate agents are no concern of this study but they are discussed at length in Foot's authoritative *Peter Kipling: The Hidden Years*).

On a second question, though, Johnson's case was stronger.

'If it's an English Journey shouldn't there be some scenery out of the window, sort of idyllic in the country bits and gloomy when you pass through towns and look at all those backyards and yearn for a lost rural England?'

'Yes, indeed. You are right. I think Paul might be too engrossed in the actual events on the train to pay much attention to the scenery during the aristocratic episode, but during the dreary ride with the estate agents, certainly. This could also afford a happy opportunity for some necessary references to the cultural history of the time, an aspect of things I have full notes on but neglected to work in I fear.'

He thereupon immediately roughed out the following, glancing rapidly from time to time at his notes on the cultural history of the year 1960.

> Doncaster to East Retford (i) Fields with cows. *Summoned by Bells* (Betjeman) (ii) Coal Mines, urban scenes, backyards: *Saturday Night and Sunday Morning*, (Sillitoe); *I'm Talking About Jerusalem* (Wesker).
>
> East Retford to Sutton on Trent (i) Fields with cows etc.: Rome, 1960 Olympic Games. 'La Dolce Vita' (Fellini) 'Rocco and his Brothers' (Visconti) 'L'Avventura' (Antonioni) (ii) River Trent: *Clea* (Durrell). (iii)

Urban Backyards etc. 'Exodus' (Otto Preminger)
Death of Kesselring.

'You see the idea?' Kipling asked. 'In the first sketch,
Paul's reflections and their cultural resonances are
pretty straightforward and parochial, that is they deal
with the English or at least English-speaking cultural
scene – Betjeman is obviously suggested by cows.
Squalid urban scenes prompt similarly fruitful but
straightforward analysis of the state of the "left-wing"
performing arts in Britain at that time. After Retford,
though, the horizons are much wider. Cows now
remind Paul of the 1960 Olympic Games though by
what precise mechanism of suggestion I have not yet
worked out. Those Olympic Games were in Rome,
which naturally causes Paul to reflect at length on the
very lively state of the Italian cinema in 1960.'

'I think I get it,' said Johnson. 'Then the River Trent
makes him think of the Nile, hence Alexandrian
Quartet, right?'

'Precisely. And the squalor of East Retford suggests
the idea "Ghetto" hence Jews, hence "Exodus" and
hence logically the recent death of the arch-Nazi
Kesselring to bring us down to earth, as it were, and also
to link us loosely back to fascistic estate agents. I think
that after Sutton-on-Trent Paul's suppressed rage at the
estate agents will drive all other thoughts from his mind,
so the socio-cultural daydream ceases abruptly at
Sutton-on-Trent.'

'That's terrific.' Johnson's admiration was unfeigned.

The Last Chapters: The Beginning of the End

It was to the furtherance of the plot that Kipling
perforce turned next. Paul, it will be remembered, had
reached Grantham on his journey towards London.
Kipling wrote a very powerful passage set in Grantham.

There was ages to wait for the London train so Paul
wandered into the street outside the station, looking

for a pot of tea and a light snack. The street was squalid. Cracked paving stones. Broken glass. Paper of all kinds blown about by the perpetual, searching wind off the fens. Blue 'Nelson', white 'Senior Service' and pinkish 'Capstan Full Strength' cigarette packets lay scattered forlornly. Transparent 'Smith's Crisps' packets, lettered in red and blue rustled, among the dog excrement of various colours. A half-shattered Tizer bottle, rolling uneasily about the pavement suddenly reminded Paul, with a jab of sadness of his little collection of bottles, labels, ration-books, gasmasks, *Sunny Stories* and other ephemera that he had had when he was five years old.

But this was home, he thought. The filth, the piercing wind, the anxious, pinched faces of the people, the starveling dogs – the pervading greyness of the town, emphasized rather than lightened by the August sunshine, this was the world that he knew, that he could feel with, feel for. After the mindless racegoers and the ratlike estate agents, the dowdy working class folk of Grantham and their squalid, windblown town felt as sunlight and clean air might feel to one escaping from a foetid cave.

'Station Café' offered snacks. The tables were of cream painted metal, chipped, covered in dirty yellow oilcloth, the wooden chairs were rickety, but the accents of the girl behind the counter, her friendly smile and even her stained green overall, with white piping and cuffs were like balm to a soul bruised by racegoers and petty bourgeoisie.

'Nowt left but fried egg sandwich,' she said. Her vowels, her honest grey eyes, her pleasant if overheavy face lightly freckled across the bridge of the nose, even her rather lank dark hair said to Paul 'Working Class' so loudly, so joyfully, that he hardly took in her words.

'Aye, that'll be champion, ey up, sithee,' he said.

The fried egg sandwich was served on a big, chipped white plate. Yolk oozed from the edges of the bread. Yolk and grease. No knife or fork was provided and Paul hesitated to ask for them.

Paul was hardly a delicately brought up boy but something about the fried egg sandwich, particularly something about the idea of picking it up and trying to manoeuvre it towards his mouth repelled him, revolted him. In that blinding moment he knew that he had been sentimentalizing the girl, the Station Café, Grantham and the whole of working class life. This oozing greasy mass was the reality of English working class existence, all else was romanticizing foolishness. With a hoarse inarticulate cry he pushed the fried egg sandwich aside, and stumbled from the café. As he half ran towards the station, the squalor of the fly-blown, wind-racked streets of Grantham looked like just that: squalor. Not 'lively' not 'honest' not 'down to earth', just squalor and filth. He knew clearly now what he had to do.

'Very powerful,' was Johnson's comment. 'We're not going to sell many in Grantham, though, are we? I mean it comes out sounding a bit like Calcutta.'

'Yes, you may superficially have a point. But it's important that Paul's revulsion from all that is symbolised by the fried egg sandwich takes place in a sufficiently repellent setting and I reasoned that Grantham is not a large town, so that no significant number of potential readers would be offended by the description, harsh though it be.'

'OK. Small point next – what exactly does Paul hoarsely cry as he pushes the sandwich away? I think we ought to specify, for the film version, or we could get the director giving him some wet and unsuitable lines. And on a film you've got to cry something, however hoarsely.'

'Yes. What about "I can't take any more"?'

'Possible. But it sounds like a preamble to suicide, which should surely lead the girl in the caff to phone the police. How about something clearly arising from the sandwich e.g. "Christ I can't eat this shit"?'

'That would be very hurtful to the waitress and I think a boy as thoughtful as Paul would be mindful of that. He is not, after all, critical of this particular fried egg sandwich, *qua* sandwich. It is a symbol merely.'

'Maybe he could explain. "Oh God, I can't eat this shit. Not a reflection on you, love, or on the chef, it's just that this whole sort of lifestyle thing is no longer *moi!*"'

'That hardly qualifies as a cry,' said Kipling coolly. 'It more nearly resembles a speech.'

'OK. So how about "Sod the working class and their fried egg sandwiches"?'

Kipling felt that this version unduly simplified Paul's attitude, but that anything more accurate would indeed be too lengthy to qualify as a cry, so with a little reluctance the suggestion was adopted.

'What,' asked Johnson, 'happens now? What does Paul know he has to do?'

'I have a difficulty about that. Basically, he decides that he must give Oxford and middle-class life a fair try, despite the horrors represented by the racegoers and the estate agents, if only to gain the means of at least choosing among the unappetizing lifestyles on offer. In my first scheme, he catches the next train home, quietly waits until October, and goes up to Cornwall College.'

'So?' queried Johnson.

'In the first place, it does not take up enough wordage. Secondly, it seemed odd that, violently repelled by working class life, Paul straightaway returns to Mexthorpe, the very acme of working classness.'

'Yes. Does sound a bit bizarre. So what's scheme two?'

'Paul goes on to London merely to spin the story out a bit and then immediately returns to Mexthorpe. A very lame expedient, I fear.'

'I don't know, though,' said Johnson, encouragingly. 'It's a new twist. I mean, working-class hero goes to London must be cliché numero uno in this sort of story but working class hero gets to King's Cross and catches next train back can't have been done too often.'

'But why does he do it?'

'Simple. He gets on train, pissed off with plebeians, also with upper crust toffs and nasty middle-class types. And then he meets nice middle-class types. Graduates. Dons, posh journalists etc., and thinks "Wow, that's for me". Bingo.'

'There are two objections to that. The minor one is that having met these amiable people, he would surely wish to maintain some contact with them, and not return immediately to Yorkshire. Secondly, your idea did in fact occur to me, but it struck me forcibly that any pleasant examples of the professional classes he met, would inevitably remind both Paul and the reader of the Brook family. This would surely cause the reader to wonder why Paul has embarked on the whole ghastly odyssey of self-questioning, encountering depressing farm labourers, aristocrats and so on, when in the Brook family he has already to hand a vivid model of a possible lifestyle – educated, cultured and yet socially responsible. Frankly I had forgotten about the Brooks, under the stress of having to find this extra twenty thousand words. I think there is a good chance that the reader will forget them too, provided his memory is not jogged. But whether my own artistic integrity can allow me to conceal and perpetuate this lapse, I am not sure.'

'God, I'd forgotten the Brooks too – the absolute models of the well-meaning wimp and pseud that Paul is going to decide to be anyway.'

'I would not have expressed it thus. But you see the problem? Should I tear up all this new material from Home Farm onwards?'

'God, no. Look, what if something had happened to drive all memory of the Brooks from his mind? Something fell on his head. An explosion. What if the Brooks turn out to have been swine? They were drug-pushers and white slavers all the time. Shattered by this revelation, Paul goes to work on a farm to find himself etc.'

'You are now reduced,' Kipling smiled sourly, 'to exactly the sort of violent and bloody plot mechanisms you once so rightly condemned when I favoured them.'

'You're right. Thinks. How about this? After the *Hamlet* bit, Paul goes to see the Brooks. Says, "I shall be off to Oxford soon, to turn myself into a trendy left wing wimp just like you lot. Isn't that nice?" Brook *père* says, all sort of sad, "Are you sure you truly want to be a wimp? How do you know you won't turn into an estate agent or a toff in cavalry twill trousers with a flat cap? Anyway, maybe at heart you really want to be a working-class slob like your dad. Why don't you go forth into, like, the world? Go to a farm and then ride about on trains for a bit to find out who you really are and that sort of thing. Return after 40 days and if you still truly want to be a wimp I will give you my blessing and my old tuckhamper I had at Radley and Balliol. If you decide you don't want to be a wimp, no hard feelings, and you'll have saved yourself a lot of bother".'

'Crudely expressed, but an exciting idea,' said Kipling. 'The quest. Almost a mythic quest, inaugurated not by the young seeker himself but by an older man, a wiser man. Not Brook, I think. More probably Uncle Ted. I am in your debt yet again. I think that what started out as a search for a mere plot expedient has given us a genuine, solid link between these new chapters and the earlier text. Also I think the initial scene of Uncle Ted sending Paul forth as a sort of Parsifal in search of a grail could be very effective.'

'Great. We could have Elsie sobbing, "Don't go, son, don't go,"' as Paul strides off and Rex and Prince howling heartrendingly. Perhaps Ailsa could come into it, like a mythic princess. If Paul comes back a true trendy wimp he gets to screw Ailsa but if he comes back an estate agent, nix. Also, lots of people could die while he's away on his endless quest, so you could tidy the place up a lot, plot and character-wise if you like.'

'He is only away a fortnight or so,' protested Kipling, 'and I do not wish to over-dramatize the quest theme.

Also, useful as your idea is artistically, it additionally means that Paul can now return straight to Mexthorpe from Grantham, his quest at an end, as I shall be very close to the twenty-thousand target, with this new material. We must think about a conclusion.'

'Yes. What you want, definitely after the quest is a really terrific conclusion. It's got to be better even than the *Hamlet* bit or people will think "I bet he really ended the book at this *Hamlet* bit and then stuck on a bit more because his publisher told him to" which is true, but not to be made too obvious.'

'Yes, indeed,' said Kipling fervently. 'I am also conscious that whereas the *Hamlet* scene looked back as it were, over Paul's life, the new conclusion should really look forward in some way – an end but a beginning, if you like, if only to form a clear contrast with the *Hamlet* scene. How could it be done?'

The Last Chapters: An End and a Beginning

The next day or so was spent by Kipling in writing a long and very moving passage in which Uncle Ted sent off Paul on the journey of self-discovery which ended at Grantham. The problem of the conclusion of *Grey Journey* then had to be faced. Johnson had already given the matter some thought.

'There are four parameters,' he said. 'One, it's got to be really good, to outshine *Hamlet*. Two, it's got to be upbeat and forward looking to look different from *Hamlet* and also to set up the sequel. Three, you don't really want to write any more of that "ee by gum" dialect stuff do you? Four, you work best when you really have your heart in it. You did *Hamlet* so well because you like Shakespeare and stuff, so what else do you really like writing about? I'll tell you: death and dogs. Don't argue, I've spent hours pulling you off killing people and writing about dogs. So hear me out. Try this – Paul gets home. Everybody in tears but nobody able to speak, so no dialogue. Why all so sad? Because Rex is dead.'

'How would Paul know that if nobody can speak?' queried Kipling sharply.

'They all point mutely to the little mound in the garden with a little cross on it.'

'They have no garden, only a concrete covered backyard. Perhaps they might cremate Rex and show Paul the urn? But how would he know whose ashes it held? Or indeed recognize the anonymous dust as ashes at all?'

'No. Better idea, the canine corpse is still laid out in the front room and they all point mutely at it. Sobs. Music from *Pathétique* in film version.'

'I thought this was supposed to be upbeat as you call it and forward looking? It could be effective, but is very sombre, surely?'

'Patience. Just before Rex died he or rather she had pups. We'll have to go back through the text and call her Rexine or something, no big sweat there though. Paul picks up one of the tiny furry bundles and muses inwardly on Time and History. By the time this pup needs a dog licence, he muses inwardly, he will have done Prelims, I mean Paul will, also South Africa will probably have left the Commonwealth. A year from now, the doglet might have pups of his own and the Russians will probably have built the Berlin Wall. Three years from now the Profumo affair will probably break, muses Paul and I will have graduated, to face who knows what unknown future and the pup will be, like, quite a big dog. Not that big, but as big as he's going to get. All the time Paul is musing the sun is gradually breaking through and Paul walks out of the house, in a dreamlike trance, Beethoven's 9th music in the film, and onto the moors. He puts the pup down and it gallops off, into the sunset. End of book, as pup pauses, briefly, in profile, to look back, on a rock.'

'We cannot call a dog "Rexine". Rexine was a kind of artificial leather used in cheap furniture,' said Kipling.

Johnson sighed. I made them some tea.

'Do you remember,' said Johnson after a while, 'that

bit in "Gone With the Wind" where Scarlett O'Hara goes into this field, just before the interval, and she's starving and she gets this carrot or something and eats it raw, looks up at the sky and says "I'll never be hungry again." Well, that was a climax for you, and yet really forward looking because true enough she never was hungry again, though she had other problems.'

'Are you actually suggesting that we send Paul back to the farm to dig up a carrot? It would have to be a sugar beet actually. And why should he do such a thing?' asked Kipling impatiently.

'No, not a carrot. Look. We stay in Grantham for the climax, right? Paul gets back from the gruesome fried egg café and finds – a small miracle! The station buffet has opened! He goes in, and finds more seeds of hope and optimism i.e. the place is run by this great, unknown chef, and he serves Paul these fantastic beef olives and tells him the recipe and Paul takes a beef olive which is broadly carrot-shaped I suppose and holds it up and looks at the sky and says "I'll never eat fried-egg sandwiches again!"'

'But he didn't eat the fried-egg sandwich in the first place. He ostentatiously spurned it,' Kipling objected with asperity.

'All right. The fried-egg sandwich sequence is OK as an idea but its not big enough. Not epic enough. It doesn't match that magnificent blasted *Hamlet* scene. Hey, wait a bit. That's it! What if we don't even try to match it, not directly anyway. What if we go to the other extreme. Lapidary. Marmoreal. Just say "Forty-two days later or whatever, Paul Kane entered Cornwall College. The end." You could start a new chapter and make that the whole of it, really sort of dignified and pregnant with meaning but very short.'

'Yes,' said Kipling, 'That sort of approach sounds possible. A little longer, I think, involving a little more detail and background, but gaining its power from simplicity, from its very lack of colour and literary pretension.'

'Great. We'll film it in grainy black and white with no music.'

Kipling set to work and rapidly produced a draft:

On the afternoon of October 10th 1960, a young man, quite unaware of the publication that day of the Monckton Report on the future of the Rhodesias and Nyasaland, was walking down a city street. His clothing was anonymous, the suitcase he carried was of indeterminate colour. He entered a low doorway. The coat of arms over the doorway was weathered and difficult to make out. He murmured something to a man of uncertain age, who was sitting at a desk. The man said something in return. The young man passed out of sight, into the deeper recesses of the great pale building.

The city was Oxford. The street was Jerusalem Street. The building was Cornwall College. The older man was the Head Porter of Cornwall College. The young man was Paul Kane.

Johnson thought for a moment. 'I think you've overdone it a bit. It just sounds as if its being described by somebody with very poor eyesight. Hey how about that? There's this fantastically beautiful girl that lives right opposite Cornwall College, only she's very short-sighted and colour blind.'

'No,' Kipling was firm. 'No more victims of handicap, no more blind people, mental defectives or deaf-mutes. Nobody with halitosis, eczema, or agoraphobia. No, no, no!'

'OK. Just an idea. You don't have to go off the deep end. But, it is a bit too, well, grey, I think. Also there's something a bit off about the rhythm of the last bit, "the city was Oxford, the street was thingy". Frankly it reminded me definitely of "The bear was bulgy. The bulge was Algy". Unfortunate, that.'

'Shall I drop this idea,' asked Kipling, coldly.

'No, basically it's great. Just a little bit more detail, a bit less well, foggy. But not a production number, keep it basically sort of lapidary, just like we said.'

Kipling set to work again:

> At 4.20 p.m., on the cool and overcast afternoon of 10 October 1960, a slim young man, aware of the publication that day of the Monckton Report, but not of its full significance, was walking down a short, narrow street. His clothing was neat, his suitcase brown. He entered a low ogee-arched doorway. The coat of arms over the doorway featured a lion and a large bird of prey as supporters though further details were difficult to discern for the casual passer-by. The young man clearly articulated his name to a stout man who was sitting at a large black rolltop desk. The stout man gave the young man a room and staircase number. The young man passed out of sight into the great, Clipsham-stone-faced building.
>
> Attentive readers of this chronicle will have divined quite easily that what we have described is nothing other than the fateful but unobtrusive entry of Paul Kane into Cornwall College, Oxford.

'Bags better. But what's with the Dickensian "attentive readers of this chronicle" stuff? It's a bit of a jarring change of style, surely?'

Kipling said nothing, but nodded, and roughed out the following alternative draft of the final few words.

> It began to drizzle as Paul Kane came to Cornwall College.

'Better,' said Johnson. 'But now it has an unhappy echo of *Rebecca*, you know. "It was raining as I came to Manderley." Also, does it make quite clear now do you think, that Paul Kane is actually the bloke in the rest of the paragraph?'

Kipling again made no comment, but quickly re-wrote the final section in quite a different form and interestingly different style:

> Most people will have guessed what the foregoing

passage was about. But some of my readers may be very young, or mentally retarded or fuddled with drink. If you fall into one or more or perhaps all of these categories let me make all clear. The young man with the suitcase is PAUL KANE, the hero as you may recall, of this book. The large building is Cornwall College, OXFORD, a big place full of books where clever people go. Do you clearly understand?

'Well it's very bold, but I think I quite like this sudden stepping out of the authorial role,' was Johnson's comment. 'It certainly ends the book on a completely unexpected note. Could you expand it a bit? I mean explain the whole passage in this savagely ironic way, not just who Paul is?'

'For God's sake!' cried Kipling, taking off his glasses and massaging the bridge of his nose furiously. 'We have taken eighty thousand words to get Paul Kane conceived, born, through school, across the Yangtze, up to the Lake District, around the East Riding, down to Grantham and up to Oxford, at every step of the way dispensing recipes and gardening hints, never missing a chance to comment on every passing navy blue blouse with white revers and cuffs and now the last thing he has to do is get through a blasted door and you won't let him!'

'Only trying to help,' retorted Johnson a shade coolly. 'Remember the old deal we made. No punches pulled.'

'Yes, yes, yes. But this is not punches, it's eye-gouging and head-butting! All I want is to go through a door. One door.'

'All right, all right. Calm down. This hasn't been all fun for me, you know. Listening to Uncle Ted droning on in bloody triplicate, e.g. But let's get it done. Let's get it bloody done. What if he had his name on his suitcase, or initials, anyway. P.K? So we say, "As the young man, er, buggered off into the building, the fitful sun caught the initials on his suitcase. P.K." They'd have to be really dumb then not to twig who it was.'

'Good. Except that working-class people in 1960 did not have their initials on suitcases. At all. Ever.'

'Uncle Ted could have lovingly but crudely inscribed them with a red-hot poker as a humble but meaningful parting gift?'

'Working-class people in 1960 had cardboard suitcases. Had Uncle Ted essayed to do what you describe, the suitcase would have smouldered or even burst into flames. Perhaps we might say that? "The extensive charring of the suitcase lid identified it unmistakably as the property of Paul Kane, for who but he would have an uncle who could in a spirit of helpfulness take a red-hot poker to what was fundamentally merely a large cardboard box?"'

'OK. No need for sarcasm. Let's just have the porter say, cheerily, "Hullo, Mr Kane, welcome to Cornwall College."'

'College porters never said anything like that to me and certainly not cheerily. Did they ever address you in such terms? Ever?'

'No. Morose lot, I thought. But look, we've alienated various groups as we've gone along e.g. Nottingham graduates and estate agents and Marks and Spencers and people who live in Grantham, so let's butter somebody up for a change, i.e. college porters. I know there's not many of them, market-wise, but —'

'It would be artistically dishonest,' interrupted Kipling firmly. There was a cold silence.

'What if a gargoyle fell on his head?' said Johnson.

'Gargoyles dropping on heads was where you were at when I first got involved in this, remember? So do it your way. You don't like my ideas, so drop a bloody gargoyle on him, making sure it strikes him in an artistically honest way, of course, have it your way.'

'That's all you can do about the really serious ideas!' shouted Kipling. 'All you can do. An idea like artistic honesty. Sneer! That's all, sneer!'

'No, it bloody isn't,' shouted Johnson. 'What I can do is get effing people through effing doors. And you can't. You can't. I can. So sod you.'

With that, Johnson stormed from the room. Kipling refused my offer of tea.

'He thinks I can't do it,' he muttered. 'The glib self-satisfied oaf actually thinks I can't get this wretched lout through a door without his help. Well, we'll see about that!'

He began to write what proved to be the final fragments of the 'lost chapters'. There passages are somewhat distressing, showing as they do the signs of a great creative intelligence struggling with a brief if severe 'writer's block', and perhaps with something darker, more fundamental. But they are part of the record, so I present them here.

> Paul Kane walked through the door of Cornwall College, that is he pushed open the door and walked through the hole or gap in the wall thus revealed. He did not of course walk through the door, as such. That is to say . . .
>
> Paul flung open the door of Cornwall College, or rather made a fair attempt so to do, but college main doors being very heavy, he not so much flung as . . .
>
> The door of college was wide open, and Paul strode, sped, marched? plodded, lurched, hurtled, careened . . . Paul slid under the door of . . .
>
> Paul, unable to solve the problem of how to get through the bloody door, because in spite of his pathetic grammar school pseudo-education and veneer of *savoir-faire* he remained at bottom a grade A working class northern prat, Paul sat on the kerb and wept. Then after a while he died. Thank God.

It was probably not long after he wrote these words that I entered the room and found Kipling staring blankly at the typescript of *Grey Journey* muttering 'Bastard! Bastard!' to himself. I was about to ask him if he would like some tea when the doorbell rang. It was the second post, with a letter from a publisher whom we had approached so long before that we had quite forgotten his existence. The publisher was willing to publish *Grey Journey* in its original sixty-thousand word version. Kipling accepted euphorically and the rest is history.

The unrefined and uncorrected fragments I have called 'The Lost Chapters' were swiftly and euphorically discarded and might well have been destroyed had I not taken it on myself to preserve them. Their existence and a hint of their content and quality is here made known to the literary world for the first time. Let us hope that some day they may be published in full, for even in their truncated form, with Paul Kane's actual, physical entry into Cornwall College suspended, so to speak, in limbo, they represent in my view material of immense critical interest.

Would, could *Grey Journey* be an even finer book with the addition of these lost chapters? Or, fine as they are, would they destroy the delicate balance of that exquisitely crafted novel? What light is shed by them on the sad breakdown in communications between the two moving spirits of the greatest partnership in post-war English literature – for it is known that Kipling and Johnson never spoke again. These are the questions posed by 'The Lost Chapters'. I hope that I have here provided sufficient evidence for the world of letters to make at least a tentative beginning to the debate.